Co...

May I Introduce

i   What is a French   16

ii   Sweet Land of Mistrust – and Credulity   23

iii   The Realm of Subdivision   33

iv   The Land of the Hand-Shake   41

v   Courteous or Gallant?   48

vi   The Case of Count Renaud de la Chasselière   59

vii   Laws of Hospitality and Gastronomy   65

viii   Martine and Ursula   72

ix   The Dear Hereditary Enemy   88

x   French as She is Spoke   99

xi   When the French Travel   107

xii   49 Million 'Sportifs'   115

xiii   France at the Steering Wheel   128

xiv   Fine Sundays   136

xv   Diabolical Inventions of the French   141

xvi   The Land of Miracles   148

Illustrations

Major Thompson	13
At Mon Repos	19
Checking the Bill	27
Civil Service!	37
Le Hand-Shake *at All Costs*	43
Passers-by: French – English	51
When Wars Were Gentlemanly	54–5
Vivisalonsection: After Rembrandt	63
'When They Get to Know You, You'll be Received Everywhere'	67
A Passion for Horses Brought Us Together	75
Miss ffyfth Gives Notice	95
'Oh, Tounet, Look over There. Isn't it Just Like Bruges?'	101
'Manoeuvres or No Manoeuvres, You Stay Put!'	120–1
Jules Introduces the English Style of Fishing	125
French Motorists – All Certifiable?	131
Technical Hitch	143
'Look, Elmer, a Statue of Ingrid Bergman!'	149

Note

The original book purports to be a translation from the English of Major Thompson.
The 'Translator's notes' are thus part of
the original French text. Some of the draw-
ings by Walter Goetz have appeared in
Punch, by whose courtesy they are
reproduced.

MAJOR W. MARMADUKE THOMPSON
LIVES IN FRANCE

May I Introduce Myself?

No well brought up Englishman (if I may be allowed the use of such a pleonasm without shocking my honourable countrymen) can, without loss of dignity, talk about himself, especially at the beginning of his story. But, like astronauts who when they reach a certain height are no longer subject to the laws of gravitation, once I am landed on the Continent, I no longer feel bound by the laws of British gravity. And since I shall have to speak about themselves to people to whom I have never been introduced, I feel freer to do what isn't done and give details about myself which on the other side of the Channel would seem uncalled for.

My name is Thompson.

William Marmaduke Thompson.

Having had the good fortune to be born an Englishman I go forward in life like a sandwich-man, preceded by my initials and followed by the little cushion whereon national honours with the passing of the years have added their alluvial deposit: C.S.I., D.S.O., O.B.E.

It is unbelievable how precious these letters fore and aft are to an Englishman: they are the inviolable frontiers of his person, protecting him like a ceremonial waterproof from too direct human contacts. When a Frenchman sends me a letter addressed 'Monsieur Thompson' I feel as if I'd caught a cold in my surname and been undressed in public, which is annoying: for after all, it is the sender who is in the wrong and I who feel I am giving offence.

I should be sorry for the French to take this remark amiss. If I venture to talk about them frankly it is because I love them every bit as much as they love the Queen of England: could anyone love them more than that? After I came out of the Army and Ursula had passed away,[1] I made my home in Paris, in the country of my second wife, so that I feel doubly privileged: I'm an Englishman nourished *à la française*.

The many sports on the fringes of which I pursued my studies (without ever seeming to catch them) did not develop me physically any more than is usually the case with my countrymen. I am fairly tall, and highly coloured in complexion: the slight parenthesis of my legs betrays the horseman. My eyes are blue and round, and a state of perpetual astonishment (especially since I've lived in France) makes them look prominent and ready to jump out of their sockets; my nose stops short and looks as if there hadn't been time to finish it, my plump cheeks shine like Canadian apples, and their ruddiness, together with the bluish line of my temples, and the white bar of my moustache make up a living reminder of the Union Jack.

When I add that my front teeth, which are slightly projecting and rest visibly upon my lower lip, make the unsuspecting (not in England where this malformation is pretty common) believe that I am always laughing and am even more jovial than my complexion would lead them to think, I shall have shamefully misused my pen to draw my own portrait.

But I must get down to speaking of the chief cause

1. Expression which the English prefer to the word 'die' especially when speaking of someone dear to them. Ursula was the Major's first wife.

THOMPSON, MAJOR HON. WILLIAM MARMADUKE, C.S.I.
(1934), D.S.O. (1943), O.B.E. (1931). *b.* 8 Oct. 1902. 4th *s.* of 4th
Earl Strawforness. *Education:* Rugby; Trinity College, Oxford.
Married: 1. 1929 Penelope Ursula Hopkins († 1931); 2. 1932
Martine-Nicole Noblet. Entered Army 1924, served Waziristan
Campaign (1924), transferred to India, Rawalpindi District
(1926), 9th Lancers Mesopotamia (1928), 38th Dogras Palestine
and Egypt (1931). Secretary to the Hon. the Political Resident,
Persian Gulf (1931). Political Agent, Kuwait (1932). Served
2nd World War 1939–45 with Royal Warwickshire Reg
(despatches twice, D.S.O., Croix de Guerre). Retired from
army 1945. Member H.M. Diplomatic Service. *Publication:*
The Arab of Mesopotamia; various communications on the
South African lepidoptera. *Recreations:* big-game hunting,
natural history, golf, gardening. *Clubs:* Cavalry (London),
Automobile Club (Paris), Honourable Company of Edinburgh
Golfers (Muirfield). *Addresses:* England: Tower Cottage,
Rowlands Castle, Pendleton, Hampshire. Continent: c/o Thos.
Cook and Son, Paris.

of astonishment in my life, which is the subject of these notes.

Now I know this will appear incredible, and yet it is the unvarnished truth: India's sun has tanned my skin; for the safety of Her Most Gracious Majesty I have roasted in the burning sands of Mesopotamia; the Intelligence (which in Great Britain is more keenly appreciated as a branch of the Services than as a quality) sent me to live in the execution of very confidential missions in Bechuanaland, in Palestine, and among the Afghans. And yet I may say today that never have I felt so far from home as now, twenty-one miles from Dover, in this fair land which bears the delectable name of France.

May the elongated beasts on the Royal Standard tear me to bits if I am lying: I feel nearer to London in the Caiman Islands than in Angoulême, and the customs of the Maori warriors seem to me less mysterious than the habits of a burgher of Roubaix.[1] So true is it that the Almighty needed only a few pailfuls of water to separate the two most dissimilar peoples in the world.

Briefly then, at a time when the whole world appears to be caught up in the vertigo of exploration, and obnubilated by the heights of the Himalayas or depths of the Pacific, it seems to me more than ever urgent to discover France.

P.S. I owe my thanks for his meritorious efforts to my friend and collaborator P. C. Daninos who is so

1. The Major had first written 'Calais'. But I pointed out to him that the name coming from an English pen was ill chosen, since the six nightshirts of the roped-together burghers still flutter ineffaceably in the sky of History. The Major agreed: 'Come to think of it, "Roubaix" is better.'

grieved he isn't English – that would have been his only chance of acquiring some sense of humour: as it is he is reduced to translating my thoughts. *Traduttore traditore*. May he never betray me! That is what I hope for but can scarcely believe. When people have been hereditary enemies for so long, something always remains in the subconscious (I saw that by his remarks about Calais). And then, believe it or not, though he has been speaking English for only twenty years he thinks he knows it. It would be equally presumptuous on my part to claim that because I have been meeting French people for a quarter of a century, I know them. The only people who claim to know such a country inside out are those who have spent a fortnight going through it, and have left with a ready-made opinion in their suit-case. Those who *live* there learn every day that they know nothing about it except perhaps the opposite of what they already knew.

i

What is a Frenchman?

In the secrecy of his Harley Street surgery a friend of mine, a famous brain surgeon, one day opened up an Englishman.

And he discovered: first, one of Her Majesty's battleships, then a waterproof, a royal crown, a cup of tea, a dominion, a policeman, the rules of the Royal and Ancient Golf Club of St Andrews, a Coldstream Guardsman, a bottle of whisky, a Bible, the Calais-Mediterranean time-table, a Westminster Hospital nurse, a cricket ball, some fog, a bit of the earth on which the sun never sets, and – right at the bottom of his subconscious, lined with age-old turf – a cat-o'-nine-tails and a black-stockinged schoolgirl.

Conscious of having committed an unpardonable indiscretion, rather than appalled by his discovery, he neither called in Scotland Yard nor the Vice Squad: he sewed him up again. And he had to conclude that all those things constitute a really good Englishman.[1] I have often wondered what my friend would find if he cut open a Frenchman.[2]

1. The Translator, at the risk of shocking certain purists by turns of phrase which are anglicisms and not French, has been anxious as far as possible to retain the aroma, he might say the *flavour*, of Major Thompson's text by keeping to the literal translation.

2. A South African girl having read about the Major's problem in her newspaper, wrote to the *Natal Daily News* of Durban which published on 20 January 1954, this curious reply: 'I know the surgeon in question and can confirm the Major's statement; I was the

What is a Frenchman?

How should one define a Frenchman?

The accepted definition of the Frenchman as one who eats bread, knows no geography and wears the Legion of Honour in his buttonhole, is not inaccurate (although the Legion of Honour when you look more closely is the Order of Ouissam Alaouite).

But it doesn't go far enough.

I am alarmed by the thought[1] that if my friend were to cut open a Frenchman he would fall dizzily into an abyss of contradictions.

Really ... how can you define these people who spend their Sundays proclaiming that they are republicans and the rest of the week worshipping the Queen of England, who call themselves modest yet always talk about being custodians of the torch of civilization, whose common sense is one of their principal exports, while they keep so little of it for themselves that they overthrow governments almost before they are set up, who keep France in their hearts and their fortunes abroad, who are enemies of Jews in general but intimate friends of some particular Jew, who love to hear their comedians make fun of retired army officers but who brace up at the slightest bugle call, who hate to

---

nurse, and saw the different objects brought out. What the Major does not relate is that the surgeon was French, and what he does not know is that I fell in love with him. One day he himself underwent a brain operation. To the general amazement, when his skull was opened there were found nineteen ex-Presidents of the Council, three dancers from the Folies Bergère, half a box of ripe Camembert, an absolutely complete Maginot Line, and several lorry loads of devalued francs.'

1. A turn of phrase belonging to the same category as the famous 'I'm afraid' so dear to the English: for example, when an Englishman knows quite well that he has forgotten something, he says he is very much afraid he's forgotten it. And if a woman who has just seen her husband set off for his office has to answer a phone call for him, she will generally say 'I'm afraid he's out'.

have their failings exposed but constantly speak ill of themselves, who say they love pure lines but cherish an affection for the Eiffel Tower, who admire the Englishman's ignorance of 'Système D'[1] but would think it absurd to declare the correct amount of their incomes to the Inland Revenue, who revel in stories of Scotch meanness but will always try to buy at a price below the marked figure; who refer complacently to their History but don't want any more *histoires*, who loathe crossing a frontier without smuggling some little thing but dislike not keeping the rules, who are anxious to proclaim that you can't take them in but rush to elect a deputy who promises them the moon, who say 'ne'er cast a clout till May is out' but cut off the heating at the end of March, who vaunt the charms of their countryside but let their builders cover it with architectural eyesores, who have a marked respect for the law courts but go to a lawyer only to find out how to get round the law, and finally, who are delighted when a great man talks to them of their *greatness*, their *great* civilizing mission, their *great* country, their *great* traditions, but who dream of retiring after a pleasant *little* life, into a quiet *little* corner, on a *little* piece of ground of their own, with a *little* wife who will be content with inexpensive *little* dresses, concoct for him nice *little* dishes and on occasion invite his friends charmingly to have a *little* game of cards?

These conservatives who for the last two hundred years cease not to slip to the left until they there re-discover their 'right', these republicans who for more than a century have repressed their royalism and taught their children with tears in their eyes the history of the

1. The Art of wangling.

At Mon Repos: The Frenchman's Dream of Retirement

kings who created France – how can a poor devil of an observer define them except in terms of contradiction?

A Frenchman? A being who above all is the opposite of what you think he is.

Admitting that, if I must try to determine the dominant feature of their characters, I would say it is: scepticism.

My old friend M. Taupin says he is much attached to the republican institutions, yet, if a deputy ends up his speech with an appeal to the great principles of 1789, he smiles ironically. It is clear he no longer believes in them. M. Taupin is a convinced partisan of peace. Yet when the representatives of the Great Powers meet round a piece of green baize to try and lay what the press-architects call the foundations of a world agreement, and then publish a communiqué which proves the *identity of their points of view,* he smiles again, shakes his head and says:

'You don't mean to say you believe *that*? . . . Words, words, words, nothing but words! . . .'

Invaded, occupied, oppressed, bullied, trailing behind him the regrets of 1900 and the gold standard, M. Taupin is a man who doesn't believe in anything because in his opinion it no longer serves any purpose to believe in anything.

After the English have waited a long time they do something. Since they don't think much, and reflect even less, they do believe in doing something.

The French don't believe in what they do. Take the Chamber of Deputies.

It looks as if they manufactured deputies just for the pleasure of destroying them. If I go with M. Taupin in a bus past the Chamber his face lights up in a sarcastic smile.

Is he a royalist? No.

What is a Frenchman?

Bonapartist? Not that either.

Does he long for a dictatorship? He has a horror of it. So what?

He is a moderate whose revolutionary spirit is confined to making him vote radical, or, if he is in a really bad temper, radical-socialist. Perhaps just as our bus is passing the Chamber, the very member elected by M. Taupin is invoking the sacred principles of 1789 and the Rights of Man. And yet he doesn't believe in them, doesn't believe in them any longer. M. Taupin declares that a man is not the same man once he has taken his seat with six hundred others. Perhaps he is right. In any case it is clear that he regards his representatives with little goodwill, rather with that eye we turn on a usurper who dares to sport a black tie with narrow blue stripes when he has never been to Eton. And it's plain from their expressions that his neighbours think as he does. It is hard to believe that it was the men travelling in the bus who sent to the Chamber the members who sit there. They seem to inhabit two different planets.

Generally the situation is summed up by a gentleman wearing a decoration:

'What we need is a strong man who would clear things up a bit in there . . . make a clean sweep.'

You might suppose the people wanted a dictator. Wrong. Let the strong man appear on the horizon, speak of reforming institutions, restoring order, establishing discipline, and for one satisfied voter you have a thousand malcontents. He is called a traitor. He wants to butcher the Republic. *Ils ne passeront pas!* They shan't get through! 1789 is invoked, and this date, which only a moment ago made M. Taupin laugh, now makes him very serious.

An impartial observer might be tempted to believe that what the French have most at heart is universal suffrage, the expression of the will of the people, republican institutions, in a word the Chamber. But you have only to pass by in a bus . . . (see page 21).

It is easy to see that, given these conditions, France is a difficult country to govern. Power slips out of hands as soon as they have grasped it. Yet foreigners are wrong to criticize the French from this point of view and accuse them of inconstancy. In my view it is a sign of good health. Many countries lose their heads because they lose their governments. The French, whose governments are certainly enough to make them lose their heads, have the incomparable virtue of keeping calm on these occasions. France is the only country in the world possessing a body which is healthy enough to allow her to live, for one month out of every four, without a head. With us a government is a necessity; in France it is a luxury which she can offer herself three, four or five times a year thanks to the soundness of her constitution and her famous common sense, which enables this admirable nation to venture without losing its balance along the most damnably difficult paths.

ii

Sweet Land of Mistrust – and Credulity

THE French are inclined to believe that other countries live with their eyes fixed on France. At least that's what their newspapers say. At the slightest crisis they write: 'Every day the foreigner is watching us.'

I must say it is rare for me to take my stand on the cliffs of Dover before daybreak to watch through a telescope how the French set about getting up![1] I think it would be indecent. Still – no doubt some damned foreigners spend all their time in such a way.

I used to wonder about this inquisitive foreigner, then I saw him in one of my rare dreams. He had one foot in the Kremlin, the other in the City, his head was British, his stomach Russian, his subconscious German, his wallet American, his memory stuffed with Waterloos and Sedans. He was watching Fair France with an international, slightly malevolent eye.

The French are convinced that their country wishes harm to no one. The English are condescending, the Americans bossy, the Germans sadistic, the Italians incomprehensible, the Russians impenetrable, the Swiss Swiss. But the French are nice. And other people are horrid to them.

1. In French: *Se lèvent*. The Major had first written *se lavent* (how they wash) but his collaborator pointed out that the French might see herein a hurtful allusion to recent statistics which revealed that the French use in a year only half as much toilet soap as the English do.
  Of course,' agreed the Major, '*se lèvent* but it's even more *shocking*.'

There are two possibilities for France.

To dominate the world by her radiance (territorial conquests, development in Arts and Letters, etc.) – these are the great heroic epochs of radiant France. Or to be invaded and conquered. Then France is trodden underfoot, massacred, crucified. These are the great heroic epochs of humiliated France.

The first condition satisfies France's pride and thirst for greatness – the Napoleonic side. From the second she draws her irresistible force of recovery – the Joan of Arc side.

It is difficult for a Frenchman to imagine that anyone can honestly see France otherwise than olive-branch in hand, a gentle prey at the mercy of bellicose nations. Any honest observer must admit that this state of mind is fairly legitimate, since three times in less than a century France has had to suffer the most savage onslaughts of the Teuton races. Still, if he can get into the right perspective for an impartial judgement and, disregarding the records of the last eighty years (mere grains of dust in History's hour glass), study the annals of earlier centuries, he must admit tnat a Spaniard whose town was sacked by Napoleon's armies finds some difficulty in considering France as an innocent victim. Foreigners should, however, realize that when a French army goes into the Palatinate or into Saragossa, it doesn't do it on purpose.[1]

Persecuted by her enemies who make war, by her allies who make peace behind her back, by the whole

---

1. This passage brought about a lively discussion between the Major and his French collaborator. 'Am I to understand that if your revered ancestor Major Raikes Hodson, in the name of His Most Gracious Majesty, with his own hands puts to death the three sons of an Indian potentate and sends their father to die in exile at Rangoon, it's all for their good?' 'In a way, yes, definitely,' said the Major.

world which steals her inventions (the French invent only to complain the next minute that the invention has been stolen), the Frenchman also feels persecuted by the French: by the government which makes a fool of him, by the Treasury which makes him pay too many taxes, by his chief who pays him too little for his work, by business men who make fortunes at his expense, by his neighbour who slanders him – in short by anybody.

This state of continual menace in which he believes he is cornered mobilizes him into a permanent condition of self-defence. That comes out clearly when two Frenchmen ask after each other. In other countries people are getting on well, or badly, but anyhow getting on. In France 'they defend themselves'.

The average Frenchman's 'I'm doing as well as I can' is the mark of a man who is perpetually on the defensive.

Yet who attacks the nice kind Frenchman? A very short word in his vocabulary to which my friend and collaborator was good enough to draw my attention disclosed the secret identity of the assailants: it's *They*. And *They* are simply everybody: the bosses for employees, employees for bosses, servants for their masters, and masters for servants, motorists for pedestrians or pedestrians for motorists, and for all of them the great common enemies, the State, the Exchequer, the Foreigner.

Surrounded by enemies even as England is by water, harassed by insatiable adventurers who envy them their lovely country, their purses, their freedom, their rights, their honour, their wives, it's easy to see that the Frenchman must be always on guard.

He is mistrustful.

Could I say he is born mistrustful, grows up mistrustful, marries mistrustfully, makes a career in mistrust and dies even more mistrustful, because, like timid people who sometimes have fits of audacity, he has from time to time been the victim of destructive fits of credulity? I think I could.

What exactly is the Frenchman mistrustful about?

From the moment he sits down in a restarant M. Taupin – who lives in the country which eats the best food in the world – begins being mistrustful of what is 'on'. Oysters, yes.

'But,' says he to the waiter, 'are they really good? You guarantee them?'

I've never yet heard a waiter answer, 'No I can't recommend them!' He might be heard to say 'They are good . . . but . . . (and he leans confidentially over his customer) . . . not your sort M. Taupin, or M. Deletange-Delbet, or M. Dupont' – which of course, especially if M. Taupin has a friend with him, sets him apart in a flattering manner.

M. Taupin knows very well that if oysters figure on the menu, it is because they are fresh, but he likes to be reassured, and above all he doesn't want to be mistaken for a man who can be taken for a ride.

M. Taupin mistrusts even the water. He calls for fresh water as if there were carafes of warm or polluted water, and he wants fresh bread, and wine that isn't corked.

'Is your Pomerol decent? Drinkable? Not just some red biddy?'

Good Lord! What would happen in a country like mine where sitting down to a meal is such a horrible adventure!

Having had a good (little) meal M. Taupin does some mental arithmetic over the bill.

Checking the Bill

'It's the principle,' he says and because he doesn't want to be done. If he doesn't find a mistake he seems disappointed, if he spots one he is furious. After all that, he leaves, more mistrustful than ever.

Some time ago when I was going with M. Taupin to the Austerlitz Station (you have to go there if you want to get to the little town in the South-West we were making for), he said he must stop at a chemist's to get some medicine.

'Too bad – don't you feel well?' I asked.

'It isn't that, but I'm suspicious of the Gascon food.'

'Couldn't you buy your medicine when you get there?'

'You never know in those little towns. I shall feel more comfortable if I buy it in Paris.'

I was surprised to find that we went past a lot of chemists that looked like quite good chemists but M. Taupin seemed to have no faith in them. And then I understood the meaning of that phrase which had always puzzled me: 'On sale at all good chemists.' Those we had passed were evidently the others.

At last he found a good one. As he came back to the taxi clasping a small bottle he said apologetically: 'I mistrust all these remedies which really serve no purpose. But my wife believes in them. By faith are we saved.'

As we approached the station M. Taupin seemed anxious and kept on looking at his watch. In the end he asked the driver for *the right time*. An Englishman or a German says: 'What's the time?' '*Wieviel Uhr ist es?*' And you tell him the time. But M. Taupin wouldn't be satisfied with any old time. He wants the right time – Greenwich time, Observatory time, Mt Palomar time. On this occasion he seemed reassured by the taxi time though it was scarcely different from his own. But when at the station he had to make a final verification in the yard because, as he explained to me, clocks outside stations are always kept three minutes faster than those inside, to hurry up the travellers. So M. Taupin set his watch three minutes behind station time and a minute fast as a matter of principle which in the end made it lose sixty seconds.

We settled into two corner seats. Then we got out and walked up and down the platform, but first he kept three seats with his hat, his umbrella and my mackintosh.

'There are only two of us,' I said.

'It's safer,' he said. 'People are so pushing!'

I thought M. Taupin felt all right about the train: he had consulted the indicator. But catching sight of an official he inquired:

'We don't change do we? You're sure?' and turning to me, 'Those indicators! I mistrust them.'

There's nothing like a train for bringing out this *They* hydra. I expected that, but this time I had more than I could take. The monster seemed to be in a state of torpor in the general somnolence, when suddenly, at the end of this dark cold day, the electric light failed.

'They might at least,' piped a little old lady of seventy with a foot warmer, 'inspect their compartments before putting them into service.' Up till then the five other French people in the compartment, taciturn, mistrustful and reserved, had been quietly reading their newspapers or their fellow travellers'. (*May I? . . . Thank you so much!*) No doubt they were only waiting for a signal – or rather the *They* sign – to dash into the fray. Like a rugby football the *They* was at once

captured by a prosperous-looking woman heavily
veiled and nursing a little dog ('*And to think they made
me take a ticket for this poor little animal!*') only to be
caught in flight and converted into a try by the right
wing, a gentleman very sure of himself travelling under
the protection of the Legion of Honour rosette, gold
watch and chain, and triple chin, all of which heaved
up and down with his sardonic laughter.

'So long as we pay!'

'To hell with everything else!'

The battle had become general. An old sporting
instinct made me regret not taking part in it. But in
my role of dumb referee I merely checked the score and
counted the *Theys*.

'If we had a government –'

'There is one but it's just as if there wasn't.'

'What we need is a government which governs.'

'You're asking too much!'

'A man with a firm hand.'

'I'd turn them all out – a good old clean up!'

'Still for the moment there they are!'

'Yes and they mean to stay!'

'All they think of is filling their pockets!'

'Grease for the palm! Jobs for the boys!'

'And journeys paid for by the state ... Did you see
about that so-called parliamentary mission to Darkest
Africa? ... Who pays for all that, I ask you?'

'We do!'

'You do!'

'I do!'

'But of course! It's a bit much! Shameful! What
country!'

'So rich!'

'And only asking to get on with the job!'

'They'll end by ruining it.'

'They're quite capable of that!'

'Look at this compartment! Isn't it a scandal? When I think of foreigners travelling! What must they think?' (All eyes are turned towards me, asking for pardon – 'England, forgive us!')

'I shall write to the Company.'

'You can write – they won't even read your letter.'

As the Ticket Inspector happened to be passing at that moment the lady with the little dog attacked him:

'It's a scandal, do you hear, a scandal! You ought to refund my ticket money!'

'If you have a claim to make, Madam,' says the Inspector, 'you must write to the S.N.C.F.'

'Then you, what are you for?'

'I look after the tickets, Madam – your ticket, please.'

The gentleman with the Legion of Honour, who was dying to intervene, threw himself into the fray:

'I must ask you to be civil to the lady!'

'I am civil, sir, and anyway who asked you? Your ticket, please!'

'I won't show it!'

'We'll see about that – if you're trying it on.'

'That's enough of that! You'll pay for that, my friend.[1] First of all' – pulling out a gold pencil on a chain – 'let me have your number.'

He drew himself up to the level of the Inspector's head, settling his spectacles and licking his pencil:

'Three thousand nine hundred and eighty-seven. Good! Well, 3987 loses nothing by waiting. Here's my ticket . . . with more to come, lots more!'

1. When a Frenchman calls another Frenchman 'my friend' it's a sure sign they're already enemies. (*Major's note.*)

The Inspector smiled, quite calm, and click-clack, punched the ticket.

'He who laughs last laughs best,' said Mr Rosette.

'Meanwhile, tickets, please!'

Grumbling, the travellers unwillingly complied. When the Inspector had gone the lady with the dog hissed through her veil:

'Tss! What a mentality! You never saw it before the War! And they're all the same!'

'Oh, worse, Madame!'

'It just shows you!'

A few moments later when I went out into the corridor to get some air, I heard the Inspector tell his mate who had just joined him:

'I don't know what's the matter with them all today. I wouldn't touch them with the clippers.'

Inspectors mistrustful of travellers, travellers mistrustful of inspectors, who in this French train, this train of mistrust, was most mistrustful?

I was still wondering when we arrived at our destination. Need I say that M. Taupin appeared mistrustful enough once he got to the hotel, especially about the beds. He poked them, felt the sheets, inspected the wardrobe. I don't think this mistrust was peculiar to him. Millions of Frenchmen are mistrustful of hotel-keepers, bills, oysters, women who lead them by the nose, army men who push them forward, politicians who hold them back, anti-militarists who would sell France to the first comer, schoolmasters who stuff the minds of their children, their enemies, their friends and, secretly, themselves.

iii

The Realm of Subdivision

Manuals of Geography and Dictionaries tell us, 'the population of Great Britain is forty-nine million souls', or 'the inhabitants of the U.S.A. total one hundred and sixty million'.

They ought to say 'France is divided into forty-three million Frenchmen'.

France is the only country in the world where if you add ten citizens to ten citizens you haven't made an addition – you've made twenty divisions.

It would be much more in Freud's line than an English major's to show why it is that these guillotiners of kings, who are everlastingly divided amongst themselves, dream of Buckingham Palace and of National Union as the one panacea for all the wounds of mutilated France. Only a war can produce that prescription, which is then called by the name of Sacred Union. The French at once call up a hundred and fifty divisions. We can't complain about that. No longer able to fight with one another, they fight the common enemy, and allow us, the English, time, according to our traditions, to *wait* a little longer and *see* a little more.

As soon as peace returns France reverts to the old conflict. In the shade of the pediments preaching Equality and Fraternity she freely flings herself into one of her favourite sports – perhaps after bicycling the most popular of all – class warfare. Not wishing to compete with the experts I'll leave it to them to explain the evolution of this sport throughout the ages, its rules and its trends. One thing, however, does strike me: the American pedestrian who sees a millionaire going past in a Cadillac dreams secretly of the day when he will be driving in his; the French pedestrian who sees a millionaire going past in a Cadillac dreams of the day when he'll get him out of it and make him walk *comme les autres*.[1]

As for enumerating all the subdivisions of Frenchmen, I give it up. But here's a pointer: for one Frenchman who wakes up in Port-de-Bouc and decides to become a nudist, you may be perfectly certain that another Frenchman arises as an anti-nudist in Malo-les-Bains.

You might think the antagonism would stop there. Not a bit. The nudist founds a society which elects an Honorary President (himself) and a Vice-President. Then the Vice-President, having quarrelled with the aforesaid President, forms a neo-nudist Committee rather more leftish than the first one. On his side the anti-nudist taking the chair at an Honorary Committee . . . etc.

The same process holds good for politics as for skiing. The fashion for short skis has just been

1. In French in the text. (*Translator's note.*) A favourite expression with the French generally followed by the word *Attendez*. Continually hearing this *Faites comme tout le monde* one might believe that in France everyone does behave like everyone else. But there's no country in the world where everyone seems so desperately anxious not to do as anyone else does, nor where people so thirsting for equality are so enamoured of favours, jumping the queue, complimentary tickets, etc.

It will be noticed that the Major carefully avoids speaking of the English pedestrian who is, of course, too well bred to dream about anything in the street.

launched. At once all skiing France has splintered into anti-short and anti-long. In the heart of every Frenchman there slumbers an *anti* ready to awaken at the approach of the mildest *pro*. This explains the inextricable puzzle of French political groups. How can a normally constituted Englishman, that is to say one just capable of understanding the difference between Conservative and Labour, appreciate all those essential shades which separate a Republican Left from a Republican of the Left, or a deputy of the *Union républicaine et d'action sociale,* from a deputy of the *Action républicaine et sociale?* Really I can't.

As I am incapable of examining the hundreds of thousands of divisions of Frenchmen (who, as we well know, hate hair-splitting), I will content myself with studying the difference which daily divides France into two camps: officials who tell you that they are always the last to be considered and are always played a dirty trick; non-officials who claim that all the trouble is caused by the officials.

The result is that every day except Sunday – day of truce when the French frankly confess that they are frankly bored – forty-two million citizens are arrayed against the forty-third.

At first sight this numerical inferiority seems to condemn the officials. But you must never judge things at first sight in France. Fresh mysteries are always coming to light. In the end you understand why these people are so incomprehensible.

The citizen who ventures into a police station or a savings bank or a Town Hall puts me in mind of a bowman setting out for the Hundred Years' War. Armed with ill-temper and equipped with sarcastic repartee, he is quite certain in advance that he won't get his way, that he will be sent from Bureau 223 on the mezzanine floor to *guichet* B on the third floor, from the third floor to the police station, from the police station to the Prefecture, where he learns that a new by-law dispenses with the necessity for producing the certificate he thought he had to have in favour of a new one which is the same as the old one only it requires fresh formalities.

Vis-à-vis this assailant, to whom the administrative vocabulary, as if anxious to put him at a disadvantage from the start, gives the name of applicant, is the official employee, generally swathed in a dim sort of overall and a suit he only puts on because he wants to wear it out.

Against the wall of this indifference (*I've seen others – if you think you're the only one. I don't make the regulations*) the arrows of the most bellicose and most decorated attackers become one by one ineffective. (*You'll hear from me again, my friend! I've a long arm.*) The long-armed gentleman produces from his pocket book a card with a red line across it, which no one has time to look at, but which produces its effect upon the public. The gentleman's long arm reaching over the official's little head pierces the office walls, crosses the Seine, makes its way into the office of the Minister who promptly sacks the delinquent.

Sheltered behind his grille the official maintains his calm: he has over his assailant that advantage which people seated in a café have over the passers-by. He feels all the more at home having made himself a little box (or in the case of the women officials a little basket), in which he keeps his or her belongings: scissors, knitting, buns, sweets, and sometimes that

Civil Service!

little rubber stamp hunted for everywhere and foolishly sought for in its right place.

It may be because my letters are often destined for distant countries, but the stamps never amount to a round sum: the young lady tells me I have to pay 93 or 112 or 187 francs, and if she finds without too much trouble the first 50-franc and the second 30-franc stamp, she has to hunt all through a colleague's portfolio for the one to make up the sum – though she may, of course, discover it in the famous little box. I've noticed that the women in post offices have a marked predilection for old cigar boxes. Good heavens! Think what a damned long journey a box of Havanas must have taken before ending up as a workbox on the table of an assistant in the Post Office!

Sometimes the combatants are separated by sheet glass perforated at a certain height by a dozen small holes. I used to believe that these holes were made to facilitate the passage of verbal missiles. Not at all! They are so arranged that never are the mouths of employee and spluttering applicant on the same level. The opponents are therefore merely reduced to shouting a bit louder. Sometimes a small opening is arranged on a level with the head of the official. That means that the assailant is forced to lower his in a movement which at once places him in an inferior position.

Through these slits, holes, or gratings, the Frenchman devotes a precious part of his existence to proving that he does exist, that he really does live where he lives, and that, since they are not yet deceased, his children are alive.

You might think that if a Frenchman isn't dead he is alive. Wrong! In the eyes of the administration he is not alive. He must first have a birth certificate, then a life certificate, sometimes both. (It's true that lately the life certificate has been replaced by a certificate of non-decease. The French are decidedly fond of playing on words, even on those words it is best not to play with.)

Having proved in black and white – if one may use such funereal terms – that he is alive, the Frenchman must then prove a great deal more, if he is planning to go to Italy and needing a passport. Strange as it may appear, a Frenchman's journey to Italy begins in his concierge's lodge; the concierge can deliver to him without delay – or later on, according to the state of her temper – the 'domicile certificate' he needs. The adult Frenchman cannot himself certify that he inhabits the house he lives in. For that he must have the seal of his concierge. After that he will have plenty of time to exhume old memories while he searches for his military-service book, which is rarely in the same place as he left it in ten years ago.

Some while back I met M. Taupin on his way to the police station. He needed a new identity card. A naïve observer would imagine that as M. Taupin has been well known and respected in his neighbourhood for some thirty-five years he wouldn't need anyone to declare that he really is M. Taupin. Still wrong! M. Taupin, in order to declare who he is, must furnish two witnesses. These two witnesses would have to be people who've known him for a long time? Again wrong! The witnesses who have to say they know him do not know him at all, but they are known to the Inspector. Generally they keep the local *bistro*[1] or grocer's shop, and by a daily trade in witnessing make something on the side.[2]

1. In French in the text.
2. There had been signs of an impending discussion between the

Such is the charmingly frank (*à la bonne franquette*) aspect of this fair land, where a smile can soften a gendarme's heart, where you can always discover a loophole in the law by which it can be evaded, and where the strict application of regulations amounts to a sanction. The important thing is the formality. I realized that the minute I set foot in France at Calais, when I heard a disillusioned Customs officer with a luscious Auvergnat accent say to a traveller guilty of two infringements:

'If this happens again I'll have to enforce the Regulations.'

Major and his French collaborator, and it flared up at this juncture. The latter having pointed out that the slowness of the English public services was proverbial, and official indifference there at least equal to that of their French colleagues, the Major said: 'Slow, I grant you. But not indifferent . . . let us say rather phlegmatic, *you know*. . . .'

iv

The Land of the Hand-Shake

For the French – and for many others – England is 'the land of the hand-shake'.

M. Taupin who, in spite of what I've told him a hundred times, always insists on making me sit in a draught, believes that he must shake hands with great violence because I am English and come from England, the land of the 'hand-shake'.

Actually, though the vigorous English hand-shake is a favourite gesture with French writers who set their detective stories in England to make them seem more real, I think the true land of hand-shaking is France.

Hand-shaking, in a way, is rather like table manners. The English have taught the whole world how to behave properly at meals; it is the French who know how to eat. The Anglo-Saxons have discovered a very evocative name for hand-shaking: it is the French who do the shaking. With us this faintly barbaric contact is reduced to a minimum. Once we have shaken hands with someone he need not expect anything else of this nature for the rest of his life.

A statistician in whose calculations I have the utmost confidence, since he is not a member of any Statistical Society and wisely limits his incursions to the neighbourhood of certain figures without ever attacking the figures themselves, calculates that a Frenchman of average importance, like M. Taupin or M. Charnelet, spends (roughly) half an hour a day (i.e. more than a whole year out of a life of sixty years) shaking hands: at nine o'clock, at twelve, at two and at six. That, of course, doesn't include the hands of people he doesn't know or visitors, relatives or friends – which would probably raise the annual total to three weeks of hand-shaking, say, three years out of a life-time. When we consider that this hand-shaker spends (roughly) three hours a day at table and eight in bed, we must conclude that the Frenchman *lives* (in the English, i.e. correct, meaning of the word) only thirty years out of sixty, which isn't enough![1]

With us this business of shaking hands has been standardized for the last thousand years; with the

---

1. A very stormy argument which at one moment threatened to bring their partnership to an end now arose between the all-too-galloping Major and his somewhat excited French collaborator.

'Your way of life,' said the latter, 'is simply deadly!'

'The English,' retorted the Major, 'prefer to die living in that way...'

'Why, then, did you come to live in France?'

'That's another story,' said the Major. 'Anyhow you must admit that the English waste less time over meals than you do.'

'They waste quite enough, when you think what's on their plates!' mused the Frenchman. 'And besides, that's not true. You take three meals a day where we only take two, and statistics prove that you absorb more calories.'

'That arises from the recognized fact that our combustibility is first class.'

'And your tea?' inquired the Frenchman.

'What about our tea?' asked the astonished Major.

'Yes, have you calculated that the Englishman who takes his early morning tea at 7 a.m., more tea at breakfast, tea in the office for elevenses, tea at lunch, tea at tea and finally a cup of tea before he goes to bed, spends (roughly) four years of his life in front of a tea-pot, which, after all, is only Chinese nonsense.'

The Major who had turned very red chose to leave the room at this juncture in order to lose his temper in comfortable seclusion. He came back an hour later, calm and having taken his revenge by ingurgitating a cup of his favourite beverage in an *English Tea-room* in the Rue de Rivoli.

Le Hand-Shake *at All Costs*

French it has various shades: it can be warm, friendly, condescending, cold, evasive, dry. Some people believe they haven't shaken hands unless they've reduced your finger-joints to pulp. Others retain the hold on your hand as if they were loth to give it back to you – use it to emphasize their arguments before letting it drop. Some keep your hand warm between both of theirs, some again seem to insinuate a soft tepid pan-cake[1] into your palm, which is unpleasant. Others offer you three fingers, or two, or the tip of one. Never mind, they are offering something and you ought to take it. I often see Frenchmen perform miraculous feats of agility right in the middle of lines of traffic in order to transfer to their left hand what they were carrying in their right, and, at the risk of being run over a hundred times, give their right hand to somebody whom this attention leaves unmoved, though, occasionally, dead.

The other evening I was watching a dramatic critic finishing off an article his paper was waiting for. Some friend came up, hesitated, then, seized with a kind of vertigo, fell upon him with outstretched hands. They couldn't help it, nor could he.

Five times in five minutes I saw him shake hands with people who said 'Please – don't get up' but who would have thought him very stand-offish if he hadn't upset all his notes and mislaid his pen in order to bid them 'Good evening'. The French are extremely touchy on this point.

Somebody would have remarked at once:

'Why, he didn't shake hands!'

'Queer!'

He would have to search all through yesterday's be-haviour to discover some detail he had forgotten which

1. The Major in a desire to smooth over the recent incident made an elegant concession and actually used the French form *pannequet*.

may have given offence. 'He didn't shake hands with me as usual' is just as serious. The supreme affront is not to take a proffered hand but leave it suspended in mid-air. When a Frenchman says, 'I wouldn't take his hand' it's like our saying, 'I cut him dead.'

A foreigner who has lived for some time in France soon acquires the habit of grasping every hand within reach. Now, when I go back to England, my forearm is continually stretching out into the void. My compatriots don't know what to do with it. Too bad! . . . It is easy to stretch out your hand but disconcerting to have to withdraw it when nobody wants it. The other day in Grosvenor Square a sympathetic Englishman did take my hand, but, come to think of it, it was probably just by chance, or perhaps he was a foreigner.

Not for nothing, indeed, was that little strip of water which separates England from the Continent called an 'arm of the sea' or '*La Manche*'. It is without doubt the frontier of the arm. Twenty-one miles of sea and a hand held out is no longer to be kissed, the arm which moved about must be kept still.

The English, from that tender age when they already appear so hardened, learn to live with their elbows close to their sides – on foot, on horseback, at table. Watch an Englishman eating. You can scarcely see his arms move. It looks as if he wasn't eating (and *can* he be said to eat?) but having his food delivered to his palate by the Intelligence Service. There ought to be a planisphere of gesture. It would show that the human arm, motionless at Bournemouth, begins to move about at Calais, is agitated in Paris, and whirls round frantically in Rome, where it becomes a thought-propeller.

It isn't only in their way of saying 'Good day' that the French appear so strange to their neighbours. What follows is equally amazing.

When an Englishman meets another Englishman he says, 'How d'ye do?' and is answered, 'How d'ye do?'

When a Frenchman meets a Frenchman he says, '*Comment allez-vous?*' and the other immediately begins to give him news of his health.

The British method seems perfectly crazy. On reflection it's perhaps more rational than the French. In the first case nobody listens to anybody. In the second, with rare exceptions, the Frenchman doesn't listen to the answer. Either he's in good health and cares little about the health of the other fellow, or else he's got a cold and the only thing he cares about is his own cold. For example:

'Still got my sciatica!'

'Ah! . . . sciatica! With me it's all down my left leg. In 1951 I went to a specialist – yes, another one! D'you know what he said? . . .'

And the Frenchman who is suffering from sciatica suffers still more because he has to keep quiet about his 1954 sciatica and listen to the other fellow's 1951 neuritis. It's the same when it comes to a good story, motor accident or business. The French are only interested in those things which happen to themselves and which are not interesting in other people. Of course this conversational selfishness isn't peculiar to them: one could say the same of other peoples. It would be true and it would be false. The English are as little interested in their neighbours as the French. But since they don't ask intimate questions about stomach-aches, impetigo or the liver (Private Enemy No. 1 with the French) they don't have to listen to the answer.

Having inquired after their respective healths, that of their relatives and children (Photos? – aren't they splendid! – I must show you mine!) the French pass on to the 'What are you doing now?' *'Qu'est-ce que vous devenez?'*[1]

Unlike the English who never ask such an agonizing question, the French really want to know. So in one minute you must explain that you are not divorced, you haven't moved, and especially that you are –

'Still with the Crédit Lyonnais?'

'Still with the United Insurance?'

'Still with the Oil Company?'

– as if your questioner were astonished they'd kept you on so long.

After this stock-taking, during which you bewail your own bad luck and the good luck of others, it's customary to make a rapid return to the health question with, 'At all events you've got your health – that's the main thing anyway' (*allez!*).

The conversation goes on for a bit and finally ends on the no less traditional 'I must fly! *Allez, au revoir!*'

I've questioned several natives on this quasi-traditional ritualistic expression *Allez!* Nobody could explain it. I suppose it has something to do with a curious invisible means of locomotion by which a Frenchman sets off when parting from another Frenchman. Really most peculiar!

Heavens! I hear the whistle of my tea-kettle. Sweet call that even the most Francophile Englishman couldn't resist. I must go and see. And I'll leave it at that for the moment.

1. In French in the text.

V

Courteous or Gallant?

EVERY French schoolboy knows that at the battle
of Fontenoy the officer commanding the French
guards, M. d'Anterroches,[1] advancing alone towards
the English, uncovered and cried:

'Messieurs les Anglais, fire the first shot!'

Every English schoolboy knows that at the battle of
Fontenoy the officer commanding the English guards,
Lord Hay, advancing alone towards the French, un-
covered and cried:

'Messieurs les Français, fire the first shot!'

As for the experts – divided as they are from birth –
they of course disagree. That's their job.

1. The Major had originally written d'Auteroche. But the Vicomte
d'Anterroches, descendant of the Comte d'Anterroches, captain in the
French Guards and hero of the battle of Fontenoy, pointed out to him
that it was beyond doubt, first that the famous 'Messieurs les Anglais,
tirez les premiers' was pronounced by his gallant ancestor and not
by M. d'Auteroche, and secondly that in the eighteenth century 'since
French was the language commonly spoken by persons of quality it
could not have been incomprehensible to English officers'.

On the first point, the Major readily admitted that the Vicomte
d'Anterroches was right, and he is supported by the Memoirs of
Marshal Saxe which are authentic. For his documentation the Major
had only at his disposal Voltaire's *Précis du Siècle de Louis XIV*, and the
testimony of eye witnesses the Marquis de Valfons and the Chevalier
de Roburent, Captain in the French Guards, and these three authors
speak of Monsieur or the Comte d'Auteroche.

On the second point, the Major is more reticent and persists in
believing that his distinguished compatriots didn't understand French
any better in 1745 than they do now.

According to some, those words were addressed to the French by one of their leaders who, on seeing the English emerge from a peculiarly British fog, cried (with this punctuation):

'Gentlemen, the English! Fire the first shot!'

Others see here a stratagem which was classic at that time when French strategists believed it was better to let the enemy use up his first cartridges so as to attack him more easily afterwards.

But many remain faithful to the classic version of this pleasing fiction, which is very French and doubly gallant.[1]

I think it only fair, however, to recall briefly the story of a French witness, the Marquis de Valfons, who wrote: 'The English officers having brought up their men to within eighty paces of the French line, halted, dressed the line and, hat in hand, saluted the French officers who in their turn uncovered.' (Extraordinary, isn't it, with what good manners they knew how to live and die in those days!)

'Then Lord Hay, cane in hand, advanced to within thirty paces of the French line, uncovered once more, and said to Count Auteroche:[2]

1. The Major plays on the words, gallant meaning *courageux* and *galant*.

2. The Major, anxious to respect the legitimate wishes of the Vicomte d Anterroches, had written d'Anterroches, but a certain M. d'Auteroche, a descendant of the Comte d'Auteroche, getting on his high horse, informed him that his ancestor was certainly at Fontenoy, that there was no *a priori* proof that he had not pronounced the historic words, and that, moreover, the Marquis de Valfons spoke of the Comte d'Auteroche.

'The least that can be said,' writes M. d'Auteroche, 'is that some doubt exists as to the copyright of the famous saying.' The Major agreed and resolved never again to put his head into this hornet's nest, and finally accepted the opinion of a French expert, Othon Guerlac, who writes in a dictionary of quotations, 'The conclusion to be drawn

'"Monsieur, give the order to fire," to which M. d'Auteroche replied, "No, sir, we never begin."'

But someone must have begun, otherwise there wouldn't have been any battle of Fontenoy, which would have been just too bad for the experts. Will this honourable company allow an ex-Major in the Indian Army to give his view? In my opinion it is possible – I would not wish to cause the French any pain – that someone may have called out to Lord Hay's troops, 'Messieurs les Anglais, *tirez les premiers!*'

But it is highly improbable that anyone on the English side understood. Every one knows that since the whole world is English-speaking, the English-man's privilege is to understand no language other than his own. And even if he does understand in no case must he stoop to letting it be believed that he does.

An objective study of the truth leads the impartial observer to conclude that this is merely one of those historic sayings invented with the sole aim of helping school-children to assimilate a conspectus of synoptic dates and fables. The most durable sayings are, of course, those which are made up all of a piece, especially when it's a question of a piece of artillery.

In the present instance, the Fontenoy saying seems to have emerged whole from the forges of French History which specialize in the coldrolling of such heroic-gallant formulae as: 'All is lost save our honour', or 'Madame, if it be possible it is done, if impossible it shall be done.'

With us the historic factories of Birmingham and Leeds, equally renowned for coldrolling, specialize rather in a noble simplicity: 'England expects that

from the divergent accounts concerning Fontenoy is that it was indeed the English who invited us to fire first.'

Passers-by: French – English

every man will do his duty' (Nelson before Trafalgar), or in the satirical and haughty saying, 'I don't give a twopenny damn what's become of the ashes of Napoleon' (Wellington), or 'What France has best taught me is the better appreciation of England'[1] (Johnson).

Both manufacturers go ahead and compete harmlessly. Their products are principally intended for home consumption. I have never found the French version of Fontenoy in English school books and I have never found a French history mentioning Wellington's remark.

If I began by speaking of the legend of Fontenoy it's because it so wonderfully symbolizes, if not the spirit of gallant courage of the French, at least the spirit they would like to have. Everyone knows that in battles there's no time to pronounce these charming sayings. The cannon speaks for the combatants. Later on historians invent the combatants' speeches.

I should be sorry to think that anyone might see in these remarks an attack upon historians. Every man to his trade. And they do theirs wonderfully. My collaborator and friend, M. Daninos, who in the last war was for some time attached as liaison officer to my battalion, told me one day at the height of the retreat from Flanders how sorry he was to be in the thick of the battle. At first I thought (and it made me feel uncomfortable) that he would rather have been at home. But no. It was that as a writer he would never console himself for not being able to describe this

1. The evocation of this saying occasioned a pretty lively sally between the Major and his French collaborator, who remarked pertinently, 'One of the things I enjoy most when I travel abroad is the thought that I am going back to France.'

gigantic encounter as well as his colleagues who weren't in the firing line.

That seems paradoxical, yet it's quite true. The historian, free from all the constraint which may paralyse the combatant – fear of the N.C.O., or even of the enemy – is the only one who can take the long view of the conflict, ignore all the killing of unimportant people, and impart the necessary colour and flexibility to his story.

Speaking of those who ought to be at a certain distance in order to treat their subject properly has led me to stray away from my own. To come back to Fontenoy. I'm finally inclined to believe that the 'Messieurs les Anglais, *tirez les premiers*' is the historic form of the very French 'After you, please.'

No, one can't consider people who don't eat keeping their elbows close to their sides, who gesticulate as they talk, talk while they're eating, or often talk about what they are eating, who, far from waiting until the ladies have left the room, hasten even with the soup to tell the most improper stories in their presence, who think they are obliged to flirt with your wife, who feel it would be rude to arrive at 8.30 when they are invited for 8.30, who kiss in public, whose men kiss each other, who never seem to finish buttoning themselves up in the streets of Paris, and hold converse with the trees when they go into the country, who never think of holding a lady's chair as she sits down at their table, who dare to call a man a murderer because he has killed four people though the police haven't yet proved it, who talk to people they don't know, especially in trains, without being forced to do so by some accident, who do not know how to brew tea, don't understand anything about cricket, try to jump the queue, who

When Wars Were Gentlemanly – 'Messieurs les Angla

ire First' is the Historical Form of 'After You, Please'

consider it a laudable feat to drive their car down a one-way street, who go out without an umbrella because it isn't raining, who in their newspapers call one of our young lords a homosexual when it would be simple to write that he accosted young men, who try to pass through the automatic doors on the Métro while they're shutting, who talk about a man's mistress before mentioning his wife, who laugh about the President's feet if they're over-large (and the *Présidente's*, too), who use toothpicks at table, which would not be noticed if they didn't spread out their left hands fan-wise in front of their mouths, who are much more anxious to hang up the receiver than to apologize when they get a wrong number on the telephone, who put on their best clothes on Sundays (except perhaps for a few I know in Lyon or Bordeaux who have an old Britannico-Aquitaine background) – no, as I say, one cannot consider these people are civilized or even polite, at least not in the English (i.e. correct) meaning of the word.

For a final example, take their attitude towards women. When an Englishman passes a pretty woman in the street he sees her without looking at her, never turns round and continues to see her 'correctly' in his mind. Usually when a Frenchman passes a pretty woman in the street, he first looks at her legs to see if she really is as smart as she looked; then he turns round to have a better view, and *eventually*[1] perceives that he is going the same way as she.

Polite? The French? Gallant rather! *De damn's hardis galants!*[2]

---

1. Not *éventuellement* (i.e. suggesting some uncertainty) but finally.
2. In French in the text.

Courteous or Gallant?

One must do them this justice: they are the champions of 'After you' – 'No, after *you*.'

The French, who as we have seen devote a considerable part of their day to hand-shaking, spend also an appreciable amount of time in asking one another to come into their houses. Some beg others to enter; the others declare they won't do so. The first then say 'Nor will I.' Since the days of Charlemagne the French have spent (roughly) three and a half centuries on their doorsteps. Astonishing that we ever find any of them in their homes!

I've always found the attraction exercised by doorsteps upon Frenchmen rather strange. Once they reach this spot they have a way of saying good-bye without going which you find nowhere in the Commonwealth, nor perhaps in any other part of the world. At the very moment when they say they must separate after a two hours' talk, they find a lot of most important things to say. It's rather like women with the telephone: the word 'Good-bye' is a signal for the conversation to be endlessly prolonged.

I was particularly struck by this attitude when, on my return to France after a long absence on a mission in Mesopotamia, I thought I must be suffering from an hallucination. There was my old friend M. Taupin in exactly the same position as I had left him six months earlier: on his doorstep still saying good-bye to M. Charnelet. My experience in the desert had accustomed me to mirages: I couldn't believe my eyes. Discreetly I drew near. I saw M. Taupin take a few steps back, raise his arms in the air, then advance threateningly upon M. Charnelet, seize him by his coat lapels and proceed to shake him backwards and forwards. It was clear – at least to an Englishman – they were on the point of coming to blows. My Major's heart stood still; I was preparing to separate them when I heard them burst out laughing. At that moment they recognized me.

'Good Heavens!' cried M. Taupin, 'here's our Major Thompson come back! What a surprise!'

I knew then that my eyes had not deceived me. At once M. Taupin asked me in, and M. Charnelet, after saying good-bye once more, on thinking it over soon joined us for a bit of a chat (*un petit brin de causette.*)

vi

The Case of Count Renaud de la Chasselière

THE English have two possessions of outstanding value: their tweeds and their silences. The silky soft density of the first is only equalled by the noble compactness of the second. I am prepared to present ten bottles of Scotch to any explorer who discovers anywhere in the world a silence comparable to that woven by a dozen gentlemen in a St James's Street club immersed in their somnolent perusal of *The Times*.

The French, who hold that silence is golden, should therefore admit without acrimony that England is a rich country. It is, above all, in our conversation that our silence is so remarkable. That's why aliens[1] find so much difficulty in understanding us.

How the devil do the English manage to keep silence while they talk?

By their 'and – er'.

'And – er', the loom on which silent conversation is woven is one of the oldest and most respected of British traditions. From time to time an Englishman may talk in a drawing-room. It may even happen – for anything can happen – that you meet a real talker. In that case he stops, realizes that no one is answering him

1. Foreigners, but the term foreigners gives little idea of the curious sensation of uneasiness and the real inferiority complex that this word *alien* confers upon its recipient. 'So you're not a British subject, you're an *alien* ...' and at once the visitor feels uncomfortable, set apart, suffering perhaps from some contagious disease.

except by grunts, and answers himself. A foreigner meeting this kind of person who cuts his monologues in two, might get the impression of a dialogue. But the well-bred Englishman, that is of course any Englishman, very soon stops talking. He makes a short pause, then from the deepest caverns of his throat emerges the 'and – er'.

With other races the 'er' implies a continuation. Not so with the English. The continuation *may* come. Generally it doesn't. What happens to it nobody knows. One thing is certain – it very rarely appears. This is the very height of reserve and discretion.

Does this mean that the English don't talk? No. Certainly they talk, but so differently from the French. In France they shine by the spoken word: the man who keeps silence commits social suicide. In England, where the whole art of conversation consists in knowing how to be silent, a man shines by his dullness.

Take for example the weather.

The French are probably past-masters in conversation but they are mere babes when it comes to the weather. That's a speciality in which the English are unrivalled. In justice to the French it must be said that they don't seek to compete with their neighbours. In France to talk about rain or fine weather amounts to a confession that one is incapable of talking about anything else. In England it is a sacred duty and the sign of a good education. To be a really good Englishman you must be able to talk about the weather – the weather we've now got, the weather we've had, the weather we may perhaps have. The word 'weather' recurs more than any other in conversation; a keyword, a commanding word; weather – rainy weather, cloudy weather, dreadful weather, stormy weather, incredible weather!

The Case of Count Renaud de la Chasselière

Probably in the beginning of things weather was created partly to allow the English to talk about it. Really there is no country in the world where it is talked of so much. Perhaps that's why it's so bad. The impressive expenditure of meteorological terms in England every day must upset the atmosphere.

That is not the only difference between a Frenchman and an Englishman in conversation. Far from it.

In France they exaggerate the smallest incident. In England we minimize the greatest catastrophe. If a Frenchman arrives at dinner an hour late because he has mistaken the day, he'll talk all the evening about his extraordinary adventure. If an Englishman arrives a few minutes late because the roof of his house fell in, he'll say he was delayed by a *spot of bother*.[1]

In England we never allow truth to enter our drawing-rooms naked (which is only another of the many aspects of our hypocrisy). In France only the bare truth is bearable. In England we take care not to allude in public to people's private lives. In France, on the contrary, they wallow in the details of their neighbour's home life.

I know that we are not exactly gentle. I know that our 'historical cruelty' has led us to do some very nasty things, especially in 16° south latitude.[2] I know, too, that in England as elsewhere people talk scandal, and that in general two women don't get on well together unless they are backbiting a third.

1. That's one of the many forms of under-statement so dear to the British heart. After a night of one of the most frightful bombings of the war, Major Thompson said to me next morning, with a smile: 'We had a bit of a picnic last night.'
2. Was the Major alluding to St Helena, or to the Boers or the Fiji Islands, all of which fall into that latitude? It was impossible to persuade him to be more precise.

But I know nothing more cruel (if we except the customs of certain Continental nations still in a state of barbarism) than a French *salon*.

The only proof I will bring forward is the strange story of Count Renaud de la Chasselière.

I had been asked to dinner by some people called Pochet. There were about a dozen guests who at first talked of this and that. That is, about everything. With the soup we discussed the cinema, then we had some existentialist trout, E.D.C. with the chicken, Four Great Powers with the salad, and flying saucers with the sweet. With the French, conversation moves about with vertiginous speed. They jump from the Hydrogen Bomb to the Roland Petit ballet, from the Kremlin to the Patinos case, and all with such ease that an ex-Major in the Indian Army finds it more difficult to follow them than a tiger in the jungle of Bengal. And what marvellous shots! Goodness! Even with his Winchester 375 Magnum my friend Basil Cranworth,[1] who was considered one of the finest shots in Assam, couldn't have brought off such results. Once caught in their fire there's no escape.

To speak of things as they are – or rather as they were, the siege of Count Renaud de la Chasselière began in the drawing-room at about 22.30 hours. At that moment the absent count was, as far as I know, still whole. All I knew about him was that he occupied an important post at the Quai d'Orsay and had conducted himself brilliantly during the war.

At 22.34 M. Pochet opened fire with, 'You know he's no more a count than I am!' – that blew off his coronet.

1. V.C., C.S.I., O.B.E., ex-officer in the 60th Burma Rifles.

Vivisalonsection: After Rembrandt

At 22.40 he could no longer be called de la Chasse-lière, it appeared he'd taken the name – and forgotten to give it back – from a place near his estate in Sologne. His name was just Renaud.

'And not even the *d*,' added one of the artillery, 'no, *-lt*'

'Like the four-horse-power Renault cars?' asked someone.

'Yes, that's it.'

'Well!' said the authentic Baron de Leaumes with a grimace.

The count was already badly damaged when at 22.50 a well-informed gentleman revealed that he had only got into the Quai d'Orsay by a fluke and never passed the Foreign Office exams.

At 22.55 a lady scored a bull by whispering that the countess had all it takes to be a nobody.

This sly shot was followed up at once by the supporting fire of one of the guests who hitherto hadn't fired a shot, and now caught the enemy in the rear, so to speak, by revealing that this father of four children had no morals at all ... in short ... !

I don't know what impelled me then – perhaps that old English mania for giving a chance to the man who is down. Inadvertently bringing the count's handicap up to its maximum I threw out a life-buoy:

'But what about the war ... didn't he do very well in the war?'

'As well as everybody else ... so what?'

We English would never have forgiven this clumsy initiative to give the conversation another turn and I could only be sorry that I had once again betrayed my mother tongue: silence.

At 23 hours precisely, the Count Renaud de la Chasselière fell – wiped out.

A sad story.

Not so sad, however, if we reflect that at the same moment, only a mile away, Count Renaud de la Chasselière with other eminent practitioners, in the course of a similar vivisalonsection, amputated the titles of the Baron de Leaumes, the Pochets and several others, so that at midnight there was nothing left of any of them.

vii

Laws of Hospitality and Gastronomy

THE French may be regarded as the most hospitable people in the world as long as you don't want to go into their homes.

Many foreigners intending to spend some time in France dream of living with a French family. After several unsuccessful attempts I've discovered that the best way to manage it – short of becoming a nurse *au pair*, which it must be admitted is somewhat difficult for a British major even if he wears a kilt – is to take up a position on the spot, find a Frenchwoman who will have you, and start your own family. That's what I did.

When you've met an Englishman, unless you shock him by an excess of intelligence or curiosity, at the end of an hour's acquaintance he will ask you to spend the week-end in his cottage. Five years later you'll discover that you don't really know whether he likes women, men or postage stamps.

At the end of an hour, sometimes sooner, a Frenchman will have told you how and why from time to time he is led to leave his wife, though *en passant* he assures you that she is *très gentille – un ange – mais voilà, vous savez ce que c'est* . . . (how on earth should I know?). At the end of ten years you will realize that you have never spent a night under his roof.

When I was going to Lyon for the first time, M. Taupin warned me: 'Now remember! Lyon society is

very exclusive – but be patient; and when they get to
know you, you'll be received everywhere.'

He was speaking only of Lyon society. I received
exactly the same advice (and every time with an insis
tence on the purely local character of this attitude) at
Bordeaux, Lille, Marseille, and even at Mazamet. *Mos
important* Mazamet. You may know Pais, Roubaix
Paris, Toulouse and Carcassonne, but you won't know
France if you don't know Brisbane-sur-Arnette, I mean
Mazamet, capital of the sheep and wollen-stocking
country. There, as elsewhere, I was told, before enter
ing fine private houses with austere façades:

'Once they've taken you in, you'll see, you'll be one
of the family!'

It's another of those vicious circles in which this
country is so rich: to be received you must be known
and to be known you must be received. The chief thing
with these exclusive societies is to begin to get into
them. It's no good 'staying shut in outside' as they say
in Limoges, when they've forgotten their latch-key.[1]

Just how long must this period of observation –
was going to say incubation – last? Impossible to say
exactly. Some say six months or a year. That's a great
exaggeration. It can last ten, twenty years. The best
thing is to prepare for the second generation which will
begin to be received, to receive, and in its turn become
very exclusive.

I must admit there is a great difference between the
provinces and Paris.

In the provinces you are at once told, 'they're very
exclusive'. You are told about the business man from

---

1. Cf. the expression *finissez d'entrer* which the Limousins use for
someone who seems to be getting congealed on the door step
(*Major's note.*)

'When They Get to Know you, You'll be Received Everywhere'

Central Europe who laid siege to Bordeaux for seven years without ever effecting a breach, or about the family from Oran which waited half a century before doors were opened to it (and which in its turn became very exclusive). In the end after all, you are received.

In Paris you are not received at all: you are taken out. The effect of the arrival of the Nicholsons or the Martinez upon their Parisian friends is really rather curious. I happened to be at the Daninoses' one day when the telephone announced the imminent arrival – I believe they spoke of the landing[1] – of the Svenssons with whom they had stayed for a fortnight in Stockholm. The announcement of a major catastrophe couldn't have caused more dismay.

'We shall have to take them everywhere!' I heard. Faced with the prospect of such a trial, my hosts seemed terribly tempted not to take them anywhere. The 'dinner at home with us' having been put off to a later date, the Svenssons were invited to have a drink at a café in the Champs-Élysées, and in the end, after some days of gaining time, taken to one of those sanctuaries of Art and Pleasure into which Parisians rarely venture unless accompanied by a foreign mentor.

I must say, in defence of the French in general and the Daninoses in particular, that the Svenssons' appetite is colossal. I don't mean for meals (though many foreigners who at home eat practically nothing simply gorge themselves when with the French) but for buildings; Gunnar Svensson is a formidable devourer of buildings. I'd always been inclined to believe that the Swedish stomach was modelled on the same pattern as any other. Not so. They swallowed the Sacre Cœur, for example, like an hors-d'œuvre.

1. The Major was, alas, right.

'Now,' said Svensson, 'we must see the Catacombs.'

If the Catacombs had been in Florence, M. Daninos would doubtless have visited them three times. But since he's lived in Paris for the last forty years, he hadn't yet been there. He remembered only that one day when he was seven years old, his father said, 'If you're a good boy I'll take you on Sunday to the Catacombs.' He couldn't have been good because he never went.

My hosts tried to dissuade Gunnar. 'Wouldn't you rather go and have a drink in the Place du Tertre?' Foreigners sometimes have fixed ideas. Gunnar wanted his Catacombs. You try and make a Swede change his mind!

'That's easy,' said his host, 'I'll take you there.' It would be most annoying for a Frenchman to confess he was unacquainted with the Catacombs. It's frightful not even to know where to look for them. On the pretext of buying some cigarettes, my friend and collaborator went off for a minute and tackled a policeman: 'What's the best way to the Catacombs?' The policeman hesitated, took out his pocket guide-book. They might have shaken hands – as between Frenchmen.

As for hospitality, properly so-called, I believe it is easier for an American to gain admittance to the drawing-rooms of Buckingham Palace than to lunch with the Taupins. On arrival he is told, 'You really must come to lunch with us. Yes, yes, indeed you must!' Weeks go by. Something unforeseen happens, the children are ill, the cook has given a week's notice. The Parisian ends by taking the foreigner, so avid for local colour, to an American grill where not even the menu is printed in French as it would be in the U.S.A.

I exaggerate no doubt. If you stay more than six months in France you are, I admit, in the end, invited by certain families. Then you are warned: 'You'll have to take pot luck.' Pot luck, an emaciated affair in England, assumes in France the most ample proportions. It explains the whole mystery: when you take pot luck with the French, and see what trouble they have taken you realize why this 'impromptu', like that of a Member of Parliament, must be prepared long beforehand. No hostess with us could achieve such a result without working at it for months. The whole question is, then, whether it is better to be invited at once by the English or to wait six months to be invited by the French. For my part I incline to the second answer. Good Lord! the meal is so good that one doesn't mind having waited so long for it.

It's not enough for their pot luck to be Pantagruelian: they start your mouth watering with dishes that don't appear on the table. When, freed from the constraint of British tact, I venture to talk about what I am eating and praise the leg of lamb *à l'anglaise*,[1] M. Taupin exclaims:

'Ah, if only you'd been here three weeks ago we'd have given you a pheasant, oh, what a pheasant . . .!'

'Actually a hen-pheasant . . . you remember Tounet?[2] It was plump . . . and melted in your mouth . . . and then, mind you, not too high, just right. Oh Major! . . .'

The French have the true gourmand's way of evoking memories of good fare which enables them to enjoy feasts in words between meals. It's an incomparable pleasure for a foreigner to be their contemplative guest.

1 Quoted in French.
2. Short for Gaston, pet name used by Mme Taupin.

On their lips the mere name of Pommard or Château Margaux emerges so rich, so velvety – already *chambré* – that you are made free at once of all the fluid treasure of Burgundy and all the secrets of the Bordeaux vines.

In this instance the pheasant – I apologize, the hen-pheasant – was there diffusing over the table the smell of game. Yet it was a leg of lamb – succulent, I must say. But with these people you soon get confused.

When a country possesses so many good things there ought not to be a close season for any of them. Only a native memory permits you to have the gastronomical calendar on the tip of your tongue. I haven't and doubtless never shall have this privilege. I realized that on my first visit to this country. When I arrived at Castelnaudary, 'You're a bit late for my little fresh livers,' said old Piquemolles. 'But I can make you a nice little *cassoulet* of preserved goose which will give you something to write home about[1] ... You don't eat it, you suck it.'[2]

'Oh yes, Mr Piquemolles – a nice little *cassoulet*.'

Then when I went on to the Pyrenees, 'It's a bit early for wood pigeon, Major,' said M. Cabrioules. 'What would you say to a nice little haunch of chamois?'

'Oh yes, Mr Cabrioules – a *little* haunch of chamois.'

Everywhere I went I was given good things to eat only to be made to regret I hadn't been given even better. Marvellous country, so different from my own where, because all the year round we eat the same things cooked in the same way, regret, like hope, is out of place.

1. Vous m'en direz des nouvelles.
2. Sic.

viii

Martine and Ursula

I HAVE experienced once in my life an upheaval comparable to what the earth must have suffered by the disappearance of the Hercynian forest or the crumbling of the Pillars of Hercules. It was when Martine said:

'I love those little silver threads in your moustache...'

We were walking along by the Seine on one of those sunny March mornings when the pastel blue sky of the Île de France behaves like a clandestine spring and begins its flirtation with the grey stone-work of the French Academy. I felt my world rocking; the corset of Victorian convention was bursting apart: I was falling definitely into the sentimental universe of the Latin nations. No longer was I 'Major the honourable Thompson, C.S.I., D.S.O., O.B.E.'. I was about to become the husband of Martine Noblet, 'You know, that incredible Englishman with the white moustache. . . .'

Across the Channel it isn't done to speak to a man about details so personal as his moustache or the mole on his cheek. (Indeed, there are so many things that aren't done in England that the unsuspecting visitor might well believe that making love was one of them.) I had to go to France to learn – in any detail – my own geography. I mean my own personal atlas, those capes and bays and valleys which interested Ursula so little and of which Martine made such a tender and accurate survey.

72

Ursula would never have spoken to me in such topographical language. I still remember the expressions used when I could not bring myself to speak:

'We two . . . after all . . . What about it?'

It is after frantic declarations of this kind that English couples marry.

That's how I came to marry Ursula.

Actually it wasn't so much love that united us as a passion for horses that brought us together.

The first time I glimpsed Ursula (there are some women who should only be glimpsed) she was riding Lazy Lassie in the Dublin Horse Show. She had a way of riding at breakneck speed over this track – with its fixed obstacles one of the stiffest in the world – and of turning round in the space of a handkerchief which attracted the most uninitiated eye. The consummate skill with which she 'negotiated the oxer'[1] was even more telling. With her hunting bowler, her tight-fitting black coat, white buckskin breeches and top boots, she was a truly brave sight. The presentation of the Gold Cup gave me the chance of congratulating her. She talked of India and of pigsticking. We soon had to part but an understanding had been created, and a few weeks later, when fox-hunting had begun and I met her again out with the Quorn, we were naturally attracted to one another.

It was the end of a gorgeous autumn and the countryside and woods of Leicestershire were still resplendent in reds and golds. Whether it was due to the beauties of Nature or our Horse Show memories I

---

1. To 'negotiate the oxer' (or to 'negotiate the hills') expressions favoured by English sportsmen. Certain French reporters are beginning to use the term, though Napoleon would have seen therein yet another mark of 'a nation of shopkeepers'. (*Major's note.*)

can't say, but in any case we lingered and lost the hunt.

As we crossed the little village of Ratcliffe we pulled up at the Marlborough Arms for a comforting whisky or even two. Then we made our way over fields and hills, gaily jumping hedges and fences and streams. We must have been about ten miles from Brookby when, to give our horses a breather and ourselves a rest, we dismounted under the trees on the banks of the River Wreak. The silence of the countryside was broken by the sound of a furious gallop. A hundred yards away we saw a straggling horseman, who looked like the young Earl of Hertford, riding like a whirlwind over the little stone bridge. A few seconds later we heard the distant call of the huntsman and the hounds giving tongue. The hunt was a long way off.

That day we were certainly not good sportsmen. Perhaps it had become clear to us both that there were other obstacles besides those of Dublin and Leicestershire we could tackle together. We sat down beside the water. I couldn't describe exactly what happened next; it was so sudden and extraordinary. The embrace sheltered by the noble oaks on Lord Cambleforth's estate was a compound of love, hunting and whisky in equal parts.

Why do so many women change, the moment you marry them? I was never to recapture the passionate moment that decided my fate. Everything changed from the minute I saw Ursula in a dressing-gown. I had been attracted by her 'presence', the way she moved, her distinction – all these qualities which were inseparable from the Horse Show, and which cancelled or absorbed the off-putting features – her long nose, large ears, prominent jaw. In time stableboys living

A Passion for Horses Brought Us Together

night and day with horses, by some mysterious pheno-
menon of mimicry get to look like horses. So in Ursula
there was something of the horse. When she was in
riding-kit the horseface didn't matter. When we were
alone together it was quite different. The amazon
vanished; only the mare remained.

At first I tried to make Ursula wear, as often as possible, the rig in which I admired her. But I couldn't
expect her to sleep in her bowler. No doubt my insistence seemed strange to her. From the day we went
into our Hampshire home Ursula gave up riding.
There was a reason for that but I only discovered it
later. Her way of laughing, of joking without restraint,
was quite changed. Evidently the fact that she now had
to look after a house and manage servants made her
more serious, more formal. She was no longer a club
friend, a comrade in competitions. She was mistress of
a house and much less ready to laugh at a joke than to
discover traces of dust everywhere – especially from feet.

'Mind your feet, dear, when you come in . . . Wipe
your feet . . . You've been in here again, Thompson,
with your feet!'

Perhaps somewhere there exists a race of men who
manage to go about without their feet. It's beyond my
powers. What is certain is that our drama arose from
feet. We always look for great motives for great
dramas. Often they are very small even though they
may be very big. Through always talking to me about
feet Ursula finally forced me to look at hers. In well-
made shoes most feet are passable. In a slipper Ursula's
foot assumed gigantic proportions – a detail which, I
may say, hadn't struck me at first because everyone said
of Ursula 'She's got a good head on her shoulders.'

(We ought to distrust these compliments; they so often hide something worse.)

How shall I describe – while keeping within the limits of decency – my life with Ursula?

Perhaps just in that one word – decency. This athlete, rough-rider, inveterate huntress, became metamorphosed into a paragon of decency.

'Now then ... Don't be sloppy, dear. Stop that nonsense ...' Of course all Englishwomen aren't Ursula, yet explaining Ursula helps to explain England. This kingdom ought really to have been Freud's; everything can be explained by the word inhibition. In the roistering days of Henry VIII or George IV this country was the scene of the most extravagant junketings and craziest orgies. The Victorian era set up a gigantic repression-enterprise and its disciples are still at it. Ursula was the descendant of a formidable bastion of the Victorian fortress. In Trentoran Manor where she was born, her grandmother, Lady Plunkwell, rigidly practised her Wesleyan principles: you must never mention the word legs (you must say 'extremities' or 'lower limbs'); even the piano legs were swathed in muslin.[1]

When Ursula was eleven she was sent to Meltenham School in Warwickshire, a school governed by the dual laws of monastic puritanism and sport. When she left, six years later, she may not have known how a boy was made, but she herself had become one.

Once again, I am anxious to guard against generalities, but I sincerely believe that if only Englishmen

---

1. Today this practice is very rarely observed: but in England it is still always safer to avoid mentioning anything that lies between the chin and the knees.

could have discovered some means of bringing children into the world without having anything to do with
women, they would have been the happiest people on
earth. The first care in British education is to separate
the two sexes as if they were never to meet again (it is
true that their relationship will be limited to the minimum). While the girls are sent to institutions where
their legs are encased in black stockings, and where
they learn to blush for the evil sins of the flesh, and
even blush at the flesh itself (at Meltenham the rule
stigmatizing nudity forced the pupils to take their
baths wearing a cotton night-dress), the boys are sent
off to schools whence they emerge to learn with amazement that besides cricket and the Colonial Office they
will from time to time, have to think about women.

It is not enough to say that nothing is done for
women. Everything is against them – themselves first
of all. It is normal that a small boy's principal aim in life
should be to become a man, but in the United Kingdom it is also the aim of every little girl. The mistresses
at Meltenham exhorted their charges to 'Run like boys,
girls, run' – which was their way of suggesting, 'That
will keep you from thinking about them.' And Ursula
ran like a boy, and the exercise purged her of the pas-
sions and evil thoughts she might have had. At a time
when Martine and her friends were becoming romantic
and reading *On ne badine pas avec l'amour,* Ursula and
her comrades were performing marvels at lacrosse and
singing, 'I'm so glad . . . I'm not pretty.'

Years may pass, worlds be overturned by wars,
governments rise and fall, but the Meltenham rule
leaves its indelible imprint upon the soul. The woman
I married carried the Meltenham mark even into the
way she slept. Some time after she had entered the

school, a mistress going the rounds of the icy dormitories one winter's night discovered Ursula sleeping rolled up in a ball under the sheets.

'My child,' she said, 'is that a decent position to sleep in? Just suppose you were to die in the night, would that be the suitable deportment for meeting your Maker?'

From that night Ursula slept according to rule: on her back with her feet out in the cold, and her hands crossed upon her breast.

I admit that's a very suitable attitude for the kings and queens immobilized in stone who sleep in Westminster Abbey under the eyes of succeeding generations. But for spending the night with a normally constituted man, there are more convenient attitudes. I should be suppressing the truth if I omitted to say that on my invitation Ursula did try to cultivate a more conjugal slumber, and go to sleep in my arms. But every time the Meltenham rule returned at night to haunt her subconscious. And if I happened to wake, I found myself alongside a statue.

I know . . . Not all Englishwomen sleep like that. Not every daughter of Albion has large feet and gigantic jaws. There are ravishing Englishwomen, and when they are pretty they make up for all those who are not. There are volcanic Englishwomen, and when the flames get going they flare up for all Great Britain and all her dominions. Ursula was doubtless a 'case'. In the Ursula 'case' love simply wasn't interesting. The storm which broke on the banks of the Wreak had passed over for ever. Shy girls may have overwhelming attacks of boldness, and then withdraw for ever into their true characters.

Sport in general, and competitive sport in particular,

never predisposed anyone to the languors of love. The Meltenham mistresses knew that, and by the intensive practice of lacrosse provided an outlet for harmful ideas. When Ursula grew up, riding took the place of lacrosse. There, again, she was unlike those rare phenomena in the jumping world whose activities in no way damp their ardour; the horse broke Ursula. I might perhaps have hoped at the beginning, seeing her abandon her favourite sport, that the calm would reawaken instincts which had grown rusty for want of use. I was wrong: Meltenham prevailed. I soon realized the meaning of the pause and what was expected of me. If she had for the moment given up riding, it wasn't for the sake of a husband, it was for England and the human race. Meltenham and her mother had prepared her for marriage in an entirely Victorian spirit. The day before she left home, Lady Plunkwell had delivered her final advice:

'I know, my dear . . . It's disgusting . . . But do as I did with Edward: *just close your eyes and think of England.*' Like her mother and her mother's mother before her, Ursula closed her eyes. She thought of the future of England. And the future of England is certainly something sacred which her children are right to care about, but somehow as far as my poor means were concerned this future was not assured. Doubtless it was decreed that the future of Great Britain would be better assured by me in France. . . .

As soon as Ursula realized that Heaven was not going to grant us its favours she returned to her training. Indeed, she took it up again with an ardour that bordered on frenzy. Rising at six, she spent the whole day with horses, stableboys, the oxer, and the Irish hurdle, on the special track I had been foolish enough to have made for her as a wedding present. In the evening, tired out, she supervised the grooming and inspected the harness. When she came in she would take off her boots, throw herself on to a sofa or her bed and sink into sleep, or else take up her cross-stitch (a fox-hunt which never got finished).

She did not refuse to do what she believed to be her duty. But at the decisive moment she always gave me a guilt complex – the feeling of guilt a schoolboy has when he is caught reading the Medical Dictionary.

'*You should be ashamed of yourself!* . . . *Put out the light* . . . *Naughty boy!*'

Was there a fire smouldering somewhere under this ice floe? I am cautious about women in general, and particularly about English women. Under a mask of coldness inadmissible yearnings may be seething. One Sunday I found Ursula reading the *News of the World,* and enjoying the carefully prepared report of one of those conjugal dramas which are the Sunday joy of even the steadiest of English homes. It was the story of an honest Liverpool tradesman who was seeking his freedom after ten years of slavery, during which his wife forced him to play at horses and drove him round the room with a whip. Ursula burst into sarcastic laughter:

'*That would suit you perfectly!*'

I don't know if it would have suited me, but the idea of a Major in the Indian Army harnessed like a pony and shaking the bells of his harness made a somewhat startling picture. I began to wonder whether Ursula's indifference was only apparent, and whether that habit of going on with her damned cross-stitch right up to the psychological moment was not, after all, the mark of a pervert.

Decades of light years lay between me and Martine's

planet, the emotional universe of the French. May I now pass on from the particular to the general and, after carefully emphasizing that England is not exclusively peopled with Ursulas, note down what I consider an essential difference between the two countries? The English observe rites for making tea, and have habits in making love. The French devote to love the care we bring to making tea. In general, love with us is a kind of rapid sketch, to be discussed neither beforehand nor afterwards. For the French it is a full-length, most carefully produced play, arranged with a prologue and intervals, and much discussed before, during, and after. The French are the gastronomes of love, the English its executants.

Far from asking, like Martine: 'Was it nice? Are you pleased? Very, very pleased?' Ursula would sooner have asked me if I felt better. In point of fact she didn't ask me anything. This behaviour, moreover, is not peculiar to Ursula; far from it. Even when they like love, the English don't talk about it. They leave that to their dramatists or newspapers.[1] Probably the loveliest love-duets in any tongue were written by Shakespeare. But his isn't the language the English use for current consumption. And if they happen to talk of love (as the French, who like to talk of and make love) they adjust their national tongue and add a little local colour to their vocabulary with imported terms like *C'est l'amour* or *Rendezvous*.[2]

1. Who have their own way of speaking of it. The *New Statesman and Nation* of 27 March 1954, quotes this sentence from an article in the *News of the World* – 'Love is a word we have got to be very careful about. In certain connections it has a sexual significance'.

2. Quoted in French. It is interesting to note that an up-to-date French girl who finds '*Je vous aime*' old-fashioned will cheerfully write, '*I love you*'.

As for the Press, it doesn't hesitate, as we have seen, to report conjugal dramas or to embroider endlessly a princely idyll, provided it is princely. Let a Royal Princess change her cavalier or lose her smile before setting out for Southern Rhodesia and all the newspapers with the largest circulation set about finding reasons for her depression. '*Why is the Princess so sad?*' and then my England, my strict soft-hearted England, so tightly laced in the corset of its traditions, always ready to be moved by a romance, all that England which feels it really owns the Royal Family, becomes passionately anxious to discover whose face it is that is floating through the Princess's imagination while she contemplates the dances of the feathered warriors of Bechuanaland. Very respectfully, but with an insistence which would be out of place in a less polite country, reporters scrutinize the sad countenance, trying to find out what is behind it. Then their austere governess, *Miss Times,* calls them to order in fifteen lines.

I have always tried to measure as accurately as possible and in every detail the distance which separates Frenchmen from Englishmen. I wish I could do this with their sentimental affairs, but my dividers fall from my hands. The barrier isn't a moat, it is an abyss.

In France a pretty woman (every woman manages to be pretty in this country, even those that aren't) would be shocked if a man didn't pay her some attention in a drawing-room, or didn't even notice her new frock. She might possibly conceive of such an attitude in a husband, while publicly deploring that he no longer sees her with a lover's eyes.

In England a pretty woman finds it 'most shocking' if a man kisses her hand, and very bad form if he compliments her on her complexion, unless of course he is her husband and then he wouldn't think of doing it.

What Martine asks of a dress is that it should be elegant. Ursula and her friends wanted something *to be comfortable in*.[1] Out of doors the Parisian wearing a new spring tailor-made is secretly delighted to see the glint it produces in a man's eye. So would an Englishwoman be of course, but such a spark is hard to imagine in a land where a man's glance, probably because of the surrounding dampness, seems to be uninflammable. Frenchmen gaze at women: Englishmen pass them by.

In France women do all they can to be noticed, while expressing great surprise if a man they don't know notices them enough to say so. A *femme du monde*[2] is scandalized if she is accosted, but bitterly disappointed if she isn't. 'I'm never followed now', she will say one day, thereby acknowledging her age and her disillusionment.

An Englishwoman can be perfectly confident on this matter: nobody will accost her. If such an extraordinary thing should happen, and some suspicious-looking foreigner thought of following her, the traditional policeman would soon restore things to their traditional order. The policemen of the two countries in this, as in other things, are very different. Martine once told me that when she was very young, but not too young to be followed, she rushed up to a policeman and said: 'Monsieur l'agent, that man is following me!' 'Sorry I can't do the same, Mademoiselle!' said the

1. I must confess that in dress Englishwomen have made marked progress in the last few years. But acquired habits stick. (*Major's note.*)

2. In France a *femme du monde* means a woman who doesn't belong to anybody (not even to her husband), probably in contradistinction to the *demi-mondaines* who belong to everybody. (*Major's note.*)

policeman, calmly continuing to direct the traffic. These are only minor differences.[1]

The real antagonism lies elsewhere. Often when a Frenchman is being spoken of you are told a little about himself, a lot about his mistress, and nothing at all about his wife. When an Englishman is being discussed you are told a lot about him, but very little is said about his wife, and nothing at all about his mistress. I am inclined to believe that a Frenchman without a mistress is like an Englishman without a club, but ... far be it from me to generalize. I am thinking only of certain town circles, though country girls often conceal under a timid exterior much more boldness than their rivals in the cities.

One thing is clear: the result of Frenchmen's predilection for a love affair, and the care they take in bringing up their children in the respect of family traditions, is that of all countries in the world France is the one in which it is simplest to live a complicated life and most complicated to live a simple life. With us the complications are rather less visible. Being without children lessens hesitations about divorce. On the other hand we hesitate longer before committing a *crime passionnel*.

An Englishman is governed by the 'it isn't cricket' law even in his sentimental embarrassments (and there's never anything comic about that even on the stage): he has to know how to part with his wife as gracefully as he would lose a game. If, 'unfortunately', he should show himself a bad loser and kill his rival, he is soon told that this is one of the things that isn't done.

1. It should be noted that if the methods of the police in Paris and London vary, their effect on 'followers' is the same; the man makes off.

He need not count on any indulgence in court. On the other side of the Channel he would doubtless have been congratulated by the jury. At home he receives a polite letter beginning 'Dear Sir' and ending 'Yours faithfully', which tells him that unfortunately and regrettably he will have to be hanged.

In France, where women have legally no rights, everything is done for women by women. The Rue de la Paix, magistracy, irony, politics, gallantry, the Republic – all are feminine gender.

In England where legally women have every right, nothing is specially arranged for women, not even men. Ships are feminine, but apart from that the masculine prevails: the greatest compliment one can pay a woman is to say that she is a good sport.[1]

That is just what they said about Ursula. We have seen how Meltenham had developed and masculinized her. In England everything works in favour of this vast conspiracy against women: the intensive practice of sport during adolescence deprives the female[2] of her

1. A good loyal friend.
2. Though much less used than the word 'woman', the term *female* in English has no derogatory implication.

It may seem strange to bring in animals when we are talking of women and love. But England is far less the land of *I love you* than the land of *love me, love my dog*.

The French eat horses and all kinds of other animals, but never miss a chance of calling one another *my little cat* or *my little sugar hen*.

The English, on the other hand, who are far more reserved about this form of address and approve of corporal punishment for their children, let themselves go in a welter of tender feelings for ponies or dogs. If a watchman at the Tower happens to break his leg by stumbling over his pike, no one takes any notice. But if Judy, a fox-terrier belonging to one of the yeomen, should fall ill, as happened recently in London, all London is moved to tears by the bulletins the newspapers publish about its health. I don't know if l'Abbé Pierre would have collected as much money over here as he did in France, but I am certain he would have collected much more if he had been

tender feelings, the clubs take away her husband, schools take away her children, ready-made clothes obscure her charms and, finally, these very charms fade.

But the age of defeat is her moment of victory. At a time when a Frenchwoman fades into a blur of greys and beiges, the Englishwoman, freed from all constraint, gaily takes her revenge on men. School uniform had suppressed her springtime, so she lives it gloriously later in life, wearing a market-garden on her head, and dolled up in baby-blue or salmon-pink dresses. Then having proclaimed her equal rights, she acts like a man, frequents her club like a man, goes into politics like a man, and, true woman that she is, becomes President of the Society for Lost Finches.

That honour was not to come to Ursula, but a still more glorious one was in store for her.

She fell at Bombay in the Viceroy's Cup, when the hurdle had been put up to six feet. She had insisted on riding a hard-mouthed Australian stallion.

After refusing the oxer Bahadur Sahib hit the wall with his chest and, far from clearing it, came a fatal cropper.

It was a complete tragedy; while the unconscious Ursula was being borne away to the British Hospital, Bahadur Sahib had to be shot.

These two faithful servants of equestrianism now repose in Indian soil.

---

campaigning for a home for stray cats. No beggar in the kingdom will contradict me when I say that a professional blind beggar will double his receipts if he is accompanied by a sad-eyed dog. Should his dog become blind, he can begin to think of retiring. (*Major's note.*)

ix

The Dear Hereditary Enemy

THE only drama in my life since the death of Ursula is my son.

First of all his Christian name. I wanted to call him Marmaduke. Since 1066 it has been a tradition with the Thompsons – who through their great-great-grandfather, can, with a little pressure on the last branch, manage to link up with William the Conqueror – to call their eldest son Marmaduke. Ursula would not have objected. But my son eventually came to me through my second wife, who is French, and my suggestion made Martine burst out laughing. The name Marmaduke always made her laugh. She says it sounds like Dundee marmalade . . . *Je ne sais pas, moi . . . pas sérieux*.

What to my mind is not at all 'serious' for an ex-Major in the Indian Army is the name 'Doukie'[1] which she made out of it. Like the good Frenchwoman she is, she can make a dress out of nothing and a pet name out of anything.

We reached a compromise; the child should be called by the first three letters of both our names and we added a c which he could do what he liked with later on. So he is called Marc. But no power in the world will stop me calling him Marmaduke to myself.

Our discussion was merely the prelude to a tragedy

1. Or on very good days Doukie-doukie. (*Major's note.*)

which gathered in crescendo with the problem of his education.

Good God! Is it really possible that peoples should have set up as near to one another as we have just for the pleasure of doing everything the other way round?

It is the same with children as with driving a car, or the judicial system: at twenty miles distance everything is the contrary of everything. The French bring children into the world to watch them grow up. Scarcely have the English seen them born than they send them away to grow up elsewhere. North of Boulogne children are brought up among grown-ups. South of Folkestone they become grown-ups among children. In France they are sentimental about them; in England they toughen them. French parents are somewhat annoyed if their sons show no signs of precocious intelligence. The English are dismayed if they show any such signs.[1]

How in such circumstances can we find some common ground?

I thought for a moment that I had found it in the person of Miss ffyfth.[2]

The boy should be brought up at first in France with an English governess. At this threat of invasion all Martine's Breton ancestry raised the alarm: she hesitated a long time over the intrusion of an artificial though consanguineous step-mother. I was supported

1. I don't mean to say that my honourable compatriots adore idiotic children. But they like children to be children. In France what they like best in a boy is the hint of the man he is going to be. An English father likes to tell you something his son said if it has a comically childish character. Unlike the Frenchman, he won't be proud if the child said something forward for his age. (*Major's note.*)
2. Without a capital. See further on. (*Major's note.*)

by some of her friends who admitted: 'Nothing like an Englishwoman for bringing up children,' and discouraged by others who said: 'Yes, all very well . . . but you won't see anything of him!'

In the end Martine agreed.

It would be inaccurate to write: 'Enter Miss ffyfth.' An icy blast from the North Sea rushed up and down the whole house. With her angular purplish face, her prominent tombstone teeth, her long arms, her bony hands with their scaly skin, Miss ffyfth was the picture of rigidity, the incarnation of the hereditary enemy, Queen Elizabeth condemning Mary Queen of Scots to death, Queen Victoria reclaiming the quagmires of vice with puritanism, Britannia in a golden helmet seated on a barrel of slaves. This lodger from the first country on the left above France installed herself as a *squatter* in our home. It was not exactly war, but the alert had been sounded. In the twinkling of an eye the situation became tense; Florine the cook was not going to make porridge for that dragon (*ça n'y avait rien à faire*), nothing doing, and Clarissa told her to her face she could starve before she got meals in her room.

I had known Miss ffyfth in India. After doing her first service in some of the swellest nurseries in the kingdom, Miss ffyfth had been summoned to Kashmir by an Anglomaniac rajah who had decided to entrust to her the training of his indolent, dreamy and rather round-shouldered son. Miss ffyfth forced this oriental youngster to wear a rod across his shoulder-blades and trained him with long hygienic walks ('Breathe deeply . . . head up . . . one two, one two') to march like one of Her Majesty's Grenadier Guards, fists swinging violently backwards and forwards. Finally, she produced a quite creditable being. When the Englishwoman left

Srinagar the boy was still an Indian, but he was straightened up; he no longer dreamed of comparing a young girl's eyes to hibiscus flowers; his indolence was discarded and he admitted that Siva had tried to perfect the monsoon in an unsuccessful attempt to test British waterproofs.

At first there were terrible battles over pronunciation. It is difficult for a child who is not completely English to admit that Beauchamp is pronounced 'Beecham' and Leicester 'Lest'r'. But nobody in the house from the boy upwards ever managed to pronounce Miss ffyfth's name correctly. It's a difficult name to whistle, even for the British. Now Miss ffyfth, who claims that she could give a course of private lessons on her name alone, is very much attached to her patronymic.

Very rare are those families who from medieval times have retained the privilege of beginning their names with a double ration of small ff's.[1] Rarer still are those who can add the luxury of a 'th'. Only a thousand years' practice can bring off this tricky recovery of the tongue without a slip. The French stumble over it and that irritates them. Old Florine remarked that she did not need such an expenditure of f's, she would manage just as well with one. '*Le jour où elle*

1. The Major is alluding to those ffoulkes, ffordes, ffrangcon-Davies and other french (no capital) old families who feel singularly *ff*ortified by this impregnable rampart, and guard their privilege very jealously. In this respect Miss ffyfth's case is very significant; if she never married it was from a desire to keep her name rather than her person intact. When she was twenty she fell in love with Merthylyd llynfartha. None of the daughters in her family had ever married a man whose name didn't begin with ff or Ff. Her father after rapidly proving that two ll's make no difference, ordered her to stop that nonsense. And so Miss ffyfth remained a virgin. (*Major's note.*)

ff . . . ra le camp, l'Anglaise, elle peut s'en coller quatre des f . . . ça ira plus vite!'

Martine, who was beginning to lose her self-control, tried to get her own back by serving up some Broglie, Maupéou, and even some la Trémouille, but the warlike Welsh jaw swallowed the old French nobility whole; that showed the hereditary enemy.

The tension increased. Martine began to realize that some of her friends had been right. After seven o'clock she couldn't see her son without having a scene. Rules must be respected. Miss ffyfth meant to dress the child, put him to bed, and get him up, as *she* wished it done, otherwise she refused all responsibility. British rule!

Martine agreed to be patient a little longer, but it embittered her character. Her mind became strangely retrospective. Hitherto she had never seemed to know who came first, the Normans or the Saxons. Suddenly she strode through the dense forest of English dynasties and hurled at my head that Gourdon who was flayed alive by Richard Cœur de Lion, as if she had just finished a thesis on the Plantagenets. At those moments she detested me. I couldn't understand, she suggested, because I was English, before all things, English.

I don't take offence for so little. When a Frenchman begins by telling me: 'I will be frank with you, in my family we have always detested the English . . .' I would wager a bottle of Scotch that he will soon assure me, 'But really we're very fond of you. . . .' For a Frenchman there are always two men in every Englishman, a good one (the Oxford *v.* Cambridge one) and the bad one (the Fashoda one). It depends upon his temper.[1] Everyone knows that the really authentic

1. The Frenchman's temper. (*Enemy's note.*)

enemy of France is Germany, but faithful as they are
to their old supplier of acrimony (who might otherwise find himself unemployed) many Frenchmen continue to hand down from father to son the idea of
the hereditary British enemy, the most steadfast and
cordial antagonist of the Frenchman in time of
peace.

To be just, it must be admitted that Miss ffyfth had
rather a special way of teaching children History.
Sometimes from upstairs I could hear her venturing
into the Hundred Years' War. 'Then King Edward III
led by one of YOUR peasants, Gobin Agache, crossed
the River Somme, and arrived at a village called Crécy,
where he made up his mind to wait and see. . . .'

And the King of England did wait. And he saw the
French knights coming. And then began the story
which was to last a hundred years of those mobile
English archers armed with wooden bows made of
supple ash, their quivers on their hips, always fresh and
nimble, and of the French knights entangled in their
armour, who charged in vain under a hail of arrows
and never had any luck with the rain. *Too bad for the
French* . . . But, added Miss ffyfth, they were *badly led;*
they were stifled under their steel helmets, and their
methods of warfare were (even then) *old-fashioned.* . . .

Often in winter after sunset I still think about the
Hundred Years' War and about those names – Crécy,
Poitiers, Agincourt, which echo in a school in Dorset-
shire like shouts of triumph, while twenty leagues away
in a Normandy *lycée* they sound the knell of French
chivalry. Then, as twilight falls and fifty proud little
English schoolboys feel the blood of the Black Prince
coursing through their veins, sadness fills the hearts of

fifty proud little French schoolboys who see John the Good (but Imprudent) led away into captivity in England. Too bad really. . . .

Meanwhile, Miss ffyfth was marching on apace into History. She was sorry for Joan of Arc who was burnt for a witch, but she was careful to point out that the tribunal which condemned her was composed of Frenchmen, and that King Charles VII did nothing to aid the girl (stupendous!). Soon she would get to Napoleon. Without even speaking of Trafalgar or Waterloo, Wellington had already beaten Napoleon at Vimieiro, remember, and finally the tiresome little man with his funny little black hat had never been able to realize his dream and go to England. For there was . . . the sea . . . *la mer* . . . and, above all, the Br . . . the Brr . . . the British navy, dear. . . .

Napoleon could only see England from afar for a few minutes on board the *Bellerophon* which was taking him to St Helena, but . . .

'But he was not permitted to land. . . .'

Not everyone is permitted to land, you see. Napoleon, however Napoleonic he might be, had to obey the British rule. Marc was probably unconvinced. Miss ffyfth was surprised by his melancholy. . . . She could not understand that a terrible global war was raging in the poor child's brain: that there was in him a little of Wellington and a little of Napoleon (with a slight prejudice in favour of the man with the funny hat – so attractive in spite of everything) and that in the French half of his mind Grouchy arrived on time at the Battle of Waterloo, while Miss ffyfth had already got Napoleon on St Helena.

Miss ffyfth's reign lasted two months. It came to an end with the third cook and sixth housemaid she had

Miss ffyfth Gives Notice

driven crazy with her unreasonable demands and her early morning tea.

One day, realizing there was something ineradicable in the French character (perhaps an anti-Miss), she departed with great dignity, having tried to *do her duty to make a real man of Marc*. But the withering look she gave me when I had been forced to surrender (it was a choice between cooks and her) – oh . . . Miss ffyfth, that damned look will haunt me even in the grave.

The 1939 war was to consolidate Miss ffyfth's territorial conquests in the tender domain of Marc. Our son was on holiday in England when the conflict broke out: we decided he should pursue his studies at a school in Shropshire.

When Marc came back to France he was completely transformed; with his cap, his grey flannel trousers and navy blue waterproof, he seemed definitely British. He had been taught that the earth is a planet on which you find England and a large heap of sand, the Sahara, which was left to the French so that they could amuse themselves with a railway they were always talking of making. He knew that the most enviable of all possible arrangements that one could ever dream of is incontestably the geographical situation of Great Britain which shelters it from want and from the tiresome promiscuity of foreign invasion. He had admitted that the French, though they might be versatile, agricultural and witty, had never been able to build really good ships, though they did what they could to become gentlemen by just once in their lives buying a hat at Lock's. Brought up under the hard law of masters ever ready to manipulate the supple cane, and of prefects quick to strike, he had recognized that the making of a gentleman begins by accepting a licking without grumbling.

Martine was surprised to find that he seemed to have an instinctive aversion for hand-kissing, and horrified when she discovered that he said, 'Good night, Mummy,' without kissing her.

A week later Marc entered a French school. There he learnt that Joan of Arc had heard real voices (not just 'voices'), that a bold seaman named Suffren had had to go right to the Bay of Bengal to find the English ships to teach them a lesson, and that in exchange for Canada and India which had escaped from French hands (*tout à la Pompadour*) England had given only very small change, a few of the lesser Antilles, together with the 5 (five) trading stations: Pondicherry, Chandernagor and the three others whose names one never remembers. Good as they were at cricket and golf, the English had nothing really comparable to the *Querelle des Anciens et des Modernes*. Finally, it was always the French who bore the first brunt in warfare, because the English took so long to dress up as soldiers.

Nine months later, exhausted by the word-for-word translation of the *De Senectute*, and the vain pursuit of the square on the hypotenuse, the poor child was nothing but a living chaos. Flung from Trafalgar Square to the Place d'Inéa, and from Waterloo Station to the Gare d'Austerlitz, he discovered that in the end men fight only for railways or cross-roads, and that the Latins in particular spend their lives in the streets named after the 29th July, or 4th September, without exactly knowing what really happened on those days.

In all this incoherence our son seemed to feel quite

lost. At all costs something had to be done to save his tottering reason.

'In any case,' said Martine, 'there can be no question of sending him back to one of your beastly English schools!'

'Nor will I,' I retorted, 'let him grow round-shouldered in one of your damned French lycées!'

In the end we sent him to Switzerland, that marvellous little country which always manages to get the best out of every war, domestic or external.

X

French as She is Spoke

I HAVE long tried to discover, without asking point blank, how to speak good French.

In pocket guides you will find: *Excusez-moi . . . Y-a-t-il quelq'un ici qui parle anglais? . . . Je suis étranger* written, to make it easier for you: *Ekskyze-mwa . . . i jatil kelkoe isi ki parle aglé? . . . ze suiz étrazé: . . .*

One such book has enriched my vocabulary with a host of expressions like: '*Garçon, le jacquet (le zake)* or *Perçoit-on un droit de péage pour traverser ce pont? . . .* (Do I have to pay toll to cross this bridge?). Its usefulness in case of need I do not deny, but I am ready to part with it at a reasonable price to any real amateur of language.

My difficulty with these handbooks – full of *tire-boutons* (tirbuto) and *harengs bouffis* (bufi)[1] so difficult to bring in at the right moment – for a time compelled me to attempt to follow the example of my honourable countrymen and adopt the lazy solution of not trying to speak French or else speaking it so badly that the French who pride themselves on 'spiking English' come to your aid and air some of the English they

1. Readers who might think that the Major is exaggerating may like to refer to the source of his information: if it amuses them they will find *un jacquet* on p. 81 of the *Mémento anglo-français* by William Savage (with key to pronunciation and appendices). As for the *harengs bouffis* (bloaters) they may be found swimming about on p. 147 of the *Travellers' Foreign Phrase Book* by J. O. Ketteridge, F.S.A.A.

99

learnt at the *lycée*: '*ze dineur iz raidi*'. This ensures, then, not only that you will not be understood but that you will not understand anybody else.

For a British subject there is a third method: not to attack the French language directly, but to try and bring your vocabulary up to date by taking advantage of such sojourns in Canada or Belgium as war or government missions may have permitted you to make. But I must warn you of the dangers of such a system.

I had put my trust in the Canadians, who assure us that they are the only people in the world who speak pure French: the French of Montaigne. Yet I would not advise any of my compatriots to ask in a shoe shop for a pair of 'claques' if he wants snow-boots, nor to ask a commissionaire for a 'char' if he wants a taxi.

The Belgian experiment if, as in my case, it precedes the stay in France, is even more dangerous. I remember the cunning expression of the house agent when I arrived in Paris from Liège, and asked if he could find me a flat '*à quatre places*'.[1] 'Facing the engine?' he inquired, and his smile showed me that I was now in the land of repartee, and perhaps about to be 'certified'.

No doubt about it, to speak really good French you must learn it in France. Surely the least I could do after marrying a Frenchwoman was to share her words. But once on the spot things became even more complicated. I knew already that north of the Ardennes there was one way of speaking French and another way south of them. I soon realized that there's one way of speaking French north of the Somme and another south of the Loire, a third east of the Massif Central, and (roughly) fifty-five other ways, so that in the end it is impossible to say exactly who in France speaks

1. The Belgians say *places* where the French say *pieces* (rooms).

French. The citizens of Lyons make fun of those of Marseilles, those of Bordeaux mock those of Lille or it may be of the Landes, the inhabitants of Nice mock those of Toulouse, Parisians mock provincials and all provincials make fun of the Parisians.

Determined to perfect my French, I set out on a long journey through France.

Experts had assured me that Touraine was the domain of the language in its perfection, so I decided to take a Touraine cure. When I returned to Paris my very British complexion (red marbled with blue veins) was distinctly heightened in colour thanks to the Vouvray I had drunk, but when at my first dinner party I ventured to say of the bourgueil that it was very *gouleyant,* meaning that it slipped smoothly down your throat, they looked at me as if I were a Yahoo. Later in the evening, under the influence of the aforesaid bourgueil, I felt emboldened to tell Martine that she was as *ameugnounante*[1] as one could wish (which for an ex-Major in the Indian Army was simply heroic) all I got in the way of thanks was her inquiry, 'Aren't you feeling well?'

Still resolved to try everything to make my French perfect, I continued my travels. Following up a certain sense of logical reasoning, I first went to visit the Tiberghiens at Roubaix whom I had got to know during the war.

M. Tiberghien received me and said, not, '*Asseyez-vous*' (take a seat) but '*Mettez-vous.*'

At first I thought he meant to ask me if I had put on woollen pants, but he merely repeated, '*Mettez-vous,*' pointing to a chair. So I put myself in it.

1. An Angevin word (formed on 'mignon') meaning attractive.

A little later when I reached Marseille I heard M. Pappalardo exclaim as he saw me, 'Remettez-vous, dear Madjor Tommepessonne'. I thought he was about to bring me a restorative, but it was merely his way of inviting me to take a seat. So I re-put myself.

The French language varies with the longitude. Still, the point is that most French understand each other more or less. But when a Basque sets about speaking the language of his corner of the earth (and he seems to take a peculiar pleasure in so doing in the presence of a Parisian or a foreigner) then, indeed, you are in an impenetrable fog. After a brief stay in Bordeaux, where I learnt that my laundry had gone to the *lisseuse* to be ironed, I was glad to get back to Paris; I felt more comfortable with Martine.

Do the Parisians know how to speak French or do they not? When at the Daninoses' I hear their little boy say to his sister, '*T'es pas cap de fair ça*' or whisper, looking at me (they must think I am more than a bit hard of hearing): 'Did you notice his moustache? Funny sort of fur! And his imper? . . . Impecc! . . .'[1] It's difficult for me to believe that this is the language of Montesq (sorry, Montesquieu).

At this rate, one may even wonder whether in fifty years' time France will not have lost half her vocabulary. You must admit that that would be 'formid' but they are 'cap' of doing it.

To come back to adult Parisians, they would be almost comprehensible to the British if many of them didn't feel obliged to garnish their sentences with

1. 'Imper' short for imperméable (mackintosh), 'impec' short for mpeccable (wizard).

truffles of Anglo-Saxon expressions which may be all right for the French, but are all wrong for the British.[1]

The other evening in a drawing-room I heard a good lady, whose words seemed to curl out through her cigarette holder, declare to a man who was holding his head in the clouds of smoke: 'I was invited to the *previou* at the *Heïmarquet Ciateur* in London. It was *auquai* (okay) ... But at the première here on Friday evening the audience was simply lousy. Nothing but '*plouks*'.

Plouks? Ploucs? Plouques? Larousse is no help here, but I think I gathered they were persons of no importance. In any case they weren't *des gens bien*.

The smoke-engulfed gentleman was surprised (in his own way):

'Jeannot wasn't there?'

'No, not Jeannot nor Marcel nor Jean. Nobody. It was deadly.'

Who were these Jeannots, Marcels, Jeans I was always hearing about in Paris? An actor, a dramatist, and a poet, all equally famous. Obviously this lady and gentleman knew them very well. Yes, intimately, as did three million other Parisians. It is smart in Paris to call people by their Christian names as soon as they have reached a certain degree of fame.

There, again, the French are the contrary of the British: you can be friends with them for ten years,

1. The Major is alluding to expressions like *footing* which to the French means *footing* (walking) but means nothing at all to the English, or *smoking* which to the British means smoking (a cigarette) and not a dinner jacket, to say nothing of the Parisian *English tea rooms* which, like the one near the Porte Maillot, put up: *Five o'clock à quatre heures*. In the same way one might cite the case of many a Frenchman who in England, having asked the way to the water-closet, is surprised to be shown the kitchen, the smoking room or winter garden, before discovering the lavatory. (*Translator's note.*)

they'll still call you Monsieur Thompson, but they readily use the Christian name for someone they don't know, and never will. We who would not hesitate to call by their Christian names people we've known only for a few hours, without thereby becoming familiar, would hesitate to say, 'Larry', when we talk of Sir Laurence Olivier, unless, of course, we were friends of his.

However, there does exist a terrain in which, without quite meeting, the smart set of both countries can fight side by side: that of the *h*. To a superficial observer England appears to be a united nation. In reality she has been divided for centuries by the war of the *h*.

One of the principal aspirations of the English élite is the aspirate *h*. An Englishman will go into training for twenty years to achieve the correct pronunciation of *Her Highness the Princess of Hanover*. I have known some who have died without achieving it. To get their own back, the common people (*gens du peuple*) avoid sounding h's when they do exist (a nice 'ouse) and put them in in all sorts of places where they don't (a hangel).

In France where this war is far less virulent, a peculiar substitution (as with us) goes with it: the *e* becomes a.[1] Only a few days ago I heard an affected girl saying with what she hoped was an English accent:

'*J'ai pris le tha chez la Pocha, c'eta parfa.*' Martine was good enough to translate and tell me that this distinguished person had taken tea with pleasure (I nearly wrote plâsir) with the Pochets. '*Parfait*', moreover, is only one of a hundred very fashionable superlatives favoured by these happy few to express appreciation of

[1]. Rather pronounced ratha. (*Major's note.*)

an evening, a film, or a play. The most often used are
Mhãrvhailleux . . . Dhivin . . . Seûblime. The quintessence
of chic seems to be to follow up these qualifications
with the word *what*. A balletomane will say, 'It's
divine, what?' – which is his way of saying, 'You're
not going to think otherwise, no?' and also a way of
dragging you along in his wake and rushing you at
high speed without waiting not to hear what you
haven't yet said.

By Jove! How the devil can an ex-Major in the
Indian Army grasp all these damned fine shades of
meaning? In this, as in other things, the French adore
a paradox. Speaking of a midge lost in the middle of a
Picasso canvas, they will say, '*C'est hénaurme*' (enor-
mous). Yet the other day when the Eiffel Tower was
being discussed I heard a lady say, 'Well, anyhow I
think it's a little darling.'

I went the other evening to one of those little
theatres where they were giving a play of the kind
called 'advanced' because you understand it only a
long time afterwards. The dialogue was crammed with
this sort of pearl:

'*Est-ce un fantassin?*'
'*Non, c'est un hexagone.*'

At each of these pearls my neighbour, who was
evidently an initiate, emitted a kind of cluck, or galli-
naceous hiccough. I saw her in the interval surrounded
by a group of connoisseurs who were spreading themselves in '*extrhaordinaire*' and '*rhe-mâr-quhâble quoi?*' In
this land of Descartes there exists an intelligentsia
which can find light only in obscurity. Someone went
past, however, some obscure *plouk*, eager for enlighten-
ment, who confessed to having understood nothing.

'But why on earth,' said my neighbour, 'must you absolutely *understand* something? How horribly bourgeois you are!'

Strange land! The workers hurl abuse at the bourgeois. The intellectuals make fun of them. The aristocracy despise them. But those who are readiest to run down the bourgeois and to feel affronted by the mere use of the term applied to themselves, are the bourgeois. And the best of it is that from plumbers to peers, including explorers, journalists and actors, the whole country, engulfed as it is in the universal wave of social security, grows more and more bourgeois every day.

France? A nation of bourgeois who try to prove that they are not by attacking those who are.

xi

When the French Travel

I SHALL always remember my visit to the stadium of Delphi. Not so much because of the majesty of the site still imbued with the Pythian mystery, but rather for the remark of a Frenchman on a cruise, who, after running his eyes over it, partly for himself, partly for his Kodak, partly for France, said to his wife, 'Doesn't it remind you, darling, of the Jean Bouin stadium?'

This strange reminiscence recalled to my memory the countless remarks made by French people all over the world: those French people who find the Passage du Havre at Milan, the Côte d'Azur in Florida or Véze-lay at St James of Compostella. When an Englishman contemplates the Bay of Rio, or St Peter's in Rome, he just thinks about St Peter's or Rio Bay. Not having such a simple mind, a Frenchman will profit by the occasion to evoke the Bay of Naples, or Chartres Cathedral.

When the English set off on their travels they take with them a sponge bag, an umbrella and even (if they are going to France) a little spirit stove for making tea. Yet a Customs official examining their brains would find nothing to declare. M. Taupin may sometimes forget his tooth-brush, but he is always armed with a voluminous case of comparisons against which, so far all Customs officials have been powerless.[1]

1. The Major believes that in a not too distant future Customs officials will possess a machine for checking up thought.

Some time ago I visited Bruges with the Taupins. 'It's extraordinary,' said M. Taupin, 'how much all this reminds me of Venice!'

Six months later in Venice our gondola, after passing the Bridge of Sighs, was making for the Fenice theatre. 'Oh, Tounet,' cried Madame Taupin, 'look over there. Isn't it just like Bruges?'

In these conditions the Taupins, who used to be very stay-at-home, and have only lately been seized with a strong tourist-appetite, normally engage in terrible souvenir-battles. By dint of talking about Bruges in Venice, and of Amsterdam in Copenhagen they are now unable to say whether in 1949 they were on the Grand Canal or the Zuider Zee.

In this Realm of Comparison meals occupy an important place: all the more so since the comparison is always made to the advantage of French (the only, *la seule*) cooking. Sure of this supremacy the French are unshakable in their demands. Madame Taupin would herself cheerfully instruct the natives about their specialities. While she is settling down to the *gnocchi alla romana* she explains so fully how she prepares it *à la parisienne* that I don't know whether I am lunching in the piazza Rusticucci or the Place de l'Alma. As for M. Taupin who is worried about his liver, he is always chasing after his cutlet: nothing so difficult to find, he thinks, as plain cooking.

'Ah,' he says, as if he were speaking of some dear dead friend, 'the good old hot-pot.'

A Frenchman's nostalgic longing for his home cooking when he is abroad has always struck me. Is it because the English do not know what it is to suffer from this melancholy that they are able to colonize the

'Oh, Tounet, Look over There. Isn't it just like Bruges?'

whole world and set up house anywhere without any regrets? Perhaps. . . .

If he is a comparison machine for the sights and food of other countries, in hotels and shops the Frenchman becomes a calculating machine. Mme Taupin has a way of using her husband as a currency-conversion apparatus which leaves me speechless. I treasure the memory of an afternoon specially devoted to footwear in the streets of San Sebastian.

'Two hundred and ninety-five pesetas, darling, what does that make?'

Darling explains that you must multiply by nine or by ten according to the rate of exchange:

'About three thousand francs. . . .'

'When I think,' muses Mme Taupin, 'that the same thing in Paris would cost twice as much . . . at least!'

They went in. And bought. Then met some other French people who had found the same thing at half the price (in the south). The strange thing is that the more the article pleased Mme Taupin the more favourable became the rate of exchange (carefully adjusted by her). With a certain pair of slippers I witnessed the fall of the peseta to 7.50, an unhoped-for affair that summer. On the other hand, M. Taupin was not so fortunate at Bilbao over a trench-coat which suited him but not Madame: that made the peseta suddenly soar to twelve francs.

'I don't want to stop you, Tounet, but really it's ridiculous . . . you'll find the same thing in Paris, only better and not so dear. . . .'

Having compared basilica with cathedrals, volcanoes with countries, rios with canals, pesetas with francs, the Frenchman then discovers fresh resources of comparison between himself and the aborigines. He looks at the world with an amused, often indulgent and readily critical eye, inclined to be the more mocking in proportion as the currency of the country is less steady. To tell the truth, no one seems to him very responsible: the Americans are grown-up children, the English golfers, the Italians spaghetti eaters, the Spaniards toreadors, the South Americans perpetual summer holiday makers. In his heart he is always asking, '*Comment peut-on être Persan?*'

The Englishman doesn't ask himself the same question, at least not in the same way. He has learnt once and for all that the world comprises Englishmen and various other tribes. In a universe which is becoming more and more mixed up, where you find Frenchmen in the Cocos Islands and Kanaks in Stockholm, the Englishman remains an Englishman and doesn't mix with anything. Twenty-one miles of sea and an historical rampart of customs and costumes keep his island free from contamination. He himself, as rarely subject to emotion as to a cold in the head, invariable as his definite article, travels across our planet like a little Great Britain in motion, inaccessible yet near, like his island. He is very much interested in the customs of all these people – so funny, aren't they? – and considers them with the explorative eye of a man who has been sent on a mission to the Zulus, sometimes even venturing to touch them with the tip of his stick or umbrella. Every now and then he is most surprised to discover among these individuals someone who really looks like a gentleman. But instead of wondering how this man comes to be a 'Persian', he muses: 'What a pity it is he isn't British!'

A magic screen brings him an indirect purified vision of the outside world: an invisible waterproof protects him from all external pollution: he emerges intact from the slums of Naples or the hordes of the Brahmaputra. Once he has crossed the frontier, the Frenchman feels obliged to justify his reputation of Don Juan from the capital of two thousand years of seduction. He wants to love and be loved. In his quality of dispenser of the generous principles of 1789, he sets out in search of adventure in the native quarters. The Englishman becomes even more reserved than these reserves, and hurries off to the tea room or to the British Club. At Bombay as at Caracas, in Havana as at Lucerne, everywhere he takes his stand on his cardinal points: bacon, tea, club, whisky. At night with the help of the Almighty he will sleep soundly in an alien land. He knows that at the slightest alarm he can count on his standing as a 'British subject' as in oldest days the Roman did on the prerogative of his status: *civis Britannicus sum.* He is assured of this by his tragic handbook under the heading *Police, complaints:* 'I've had my wallet . . . bag . . . cloak . . . stolen . . . Stop thief. Fire! . . . Help! . . . Drive me to the British Consulate!' One knows that at once the Foreign Office, Scotland Yard and the Intelligence Service will be on their toes. Should the situation worsen and degenerate into a riot, it will be made known that H.M.S. *Revenge*, steaming towards Aden, is bringing protection to Mr Smith.

Perhaps M. Taupin does not feel so sure about his consuls and their powers? While I detest being cluttered up with papers he loves to set out with letters of recommendation. Acquired at the cost of manifold negotiations, these credentials inform the Duke of

Rovedrego, the Alcade of Grenada or the Commenda-
tore Ruspolo di Ruspoli that M. Taupin is travelling
for his pleasure. They are all, of course, important
people, and since they possess several residences,
châteaux or country houses, are always away. Never
mind, with all these damned letters which will have no
effect upon their addressees, even when they do reach
them, M. Taupin feels happier. You never know![1]

That is how M. Taupin travels. It would be more
accurate to say it is how France travels. For what M.
Taupin exports with him is the whole of France. An
Englishman, convinced as he is of his superiority, con-
tents himself with making it felt (pretty disagreeably
at times). The Frenchman is equally convinced of the
superiority of his own country; he himself is *La France
spirituelle,* gallant France, the France of freedom,
Vercingetorix and Christian Dior, Pascal and the Rue
de la Paix. He who, at home, seizes on any pretext for
disparaging his corporate bodies, who in Paris would
rather boost a detective story signed W. A. Thorndyke
than one signed J. Dupont,[2] now defends France, her
artists, her inventors, with all the fervour of a Cru-
sader. And who would dream of attacking him? Hotel
managers, restaurant keepers, drift towards him to
inhale a little Parisian air.[3] And M. Taupin receives
them on his ambulant territory with good-humoured
gratification. The restaurant keeper says, 'Ah, France!'

1. It does sometimes happen that one of these people is 'touched'
in the postal or affective sense of the word by a letter. He may even
occasionally keep his guest for lunch, dinner or between meals, so
that M. Taupin, being received as no one is received in Paris, has no
time left to see the countryside, which is just too bad. (*Major's note.*)

2. M. Daninos confided to me that he became known far more
quickly as the translator of Major Thompson than when he wrote
under his own name. (*Major's note.*)

3. Abroad every Frenchman comes from Paris. (*Major's note.*)

and M. Taupin says, 'Ah! . . .' Then his interlocutor sighs, 'Ah! Paris!' and M. Taupin replies, 'Ah! . . .' And so from Ah! to Ah! the dialogue continues. The whole world melts away, only Paris remains.

'There's nothing like it anyway!' says M. Taupin.

'I lived in the Rua des Chiseaux,' states the Italian.

'Ah,' sighs M. Taupin, 'the good old Rue des Ciseaux!' (He confesses afterwards that it is the first time he ever heard of it.)

'*La Torre di Aiffel!*'

'Ah! The Eiffel Tower!'

'*Les Folies Bergère! . . .*'

A touching moment, when after a rather naughtier *ah!* M. Taupin and the restaurant keeper exchange a sly wink. Then M. Taupin, generous and chivalrous, concludes with:

'Every man has two countries, his own and then France . . .'

But the foreigner must be on his guard if one day he takes this saying literally and decides to become naturalized. He may be reminded pretty quickly that the second country isn't the first, and if he isn't satisfied . . .

After all, France for the French!

xii

49 Million 'Sportifs'

THERE are many good moments for visiting France
but there is one which might possibly give you a
wrong idea: the period from about the 1st to the 25th
July. One of my first travels in France took place
during that period. I had come from Gibraltar, crossed
the Pyrenees and was on my way to Paris, when I was
stopped by two gendarmes at a cross-roads:

'You can't go through!' they said.

At that time I still retained the English habit of
never asking questions, so I complied without asking
why. The sight of a grand array of police encouraged
me to think that a bandit was about to be rounded up.
However, perceiving on the Route Nationale a great
crowd conversing gaily with the mounted police, I
concluded that the affair must be less dramatic. A
column of armoured cars drawn up on the other side,
at one of the cross-roads, led me to believe for a
moment that there was going to be a march past of
the army. Evidently not, because I soon heard the
captain of the gendarmes say to a young lieutenant
who was showing his impatience by slapping his boot
with his cane (his men didn't seem to mind nearly so
much):

'Manoeuvres or no manoeuvres, you stay put!'

It was indeed clear that no one would get through,
not the French with their armoured cars, nor Major

Thompson with his car, nor even the gentleman who extricated his important person from his important automobile, police pass in hand and was merely told: 'Do as the rest do. Wait!' – words which I was to hear fairly often during what followed. From all these premises I had deduced that all traffic was held up to leave the way free for the President of the Republic and his suite, when a great cry burst from countless throats:

'There they are! That's them!'

This singular plural led me to suppose for a moment that the Head of the State was about to appear with my Most Gracious Sovereigns, who were then in France. Imagine my surprise on seeing emerge, instead of Gracious Sovereigns, two male individuals, gracelessly swaying on their bicycles, festooned with inner tubes and tyres and clad in glaring jerseys and exiguous shorts, covered with mud, altogether rather a shocking sight. The spectators were kind enough to explain to me – without my asking – that these fellows were doing a bicycle Tour of France, and getting to Paris as quickly as possible by the slowest roads, which seemed to me strange. But, after all, these are things about which an Englishman, who is never astonished at anything, should not express any tactless surprise. From time to time in London a citizen may, from love of sport or to satisfy some whim, walk down Piccadilly in a red blazer and white shorts, but it would be the worst of bad taste to turn round and look at him. Everyone is free to act and dress as he pleases without fear of being noticed in a country where good taste demands that we should see people without looking at them.

What amazed me in this instance was not so much

the careless dress of these gentlemen as the fact that the police brought all traffic to a standstill for them, and for a line of lorries belonging to suppliers of *pâtés* and *apéritifs* which at first sight had nothing to do with these proceedings, but were – as inquiry revealed – closely connected with them. I know that there is the same sort of Tour of England, but how different it is! Our racing cyclists, far from stopping the traffic, follow it; they stop at the red lights *comme tout le monde*. They are only amateurs who, protected by public announcements, apologize for passing one another, and get off their bicycles to have tea. Above all, these young men, of whom no one takes any notice, are properly dressed.[1]

I didn't reach Paris till late that night. I was worried about the situation in Bengal, where – for reasons too long to explain, and, moreover, no one else's concern – I had had to leave Ursula. There were threats of a rising in Calcutta, the police had had to open fire on the mob, and eventually there had been two hundred killed.

I had already heard that much in Gibraltar, but I wanted to know more. So I bought the Late Night, and even the Late Night Special, editions, of an evening paper, where spread across eight columns a heading announced:

GARRALDI ET BIQUET ENSEMBLE DEVANT LES JUGES DE PAIX

Thinking that an important action was drawing to

---

1. The Major is anxious to emphasize in this connexion that 'shorts', though they mean 'courts' in French, are nevertheless long. When a rugby player's knickers are torn in a scrum, and have to be replaced at once, the player is immediately surrounded by members

its close, I prepared to read the speeches under the alluring sub-title, *The Florentine demon is betrayed by his servants*, when my eye was attracted to the cross-section map of the Pyrenees which spread across the southern corner of the paper. I learned later that Garraldi and Biquet were the heroes of the Tour de France, and that by *juges de paix* (magistrates) one should understand, by one of those metaphors so dear to the hearts of French sport-chroniclers, le Tourmalet and l'Aubisque; the 'demon' was the man in the yellow sweater, and the 'servants' the men in his team. As for the two hundred dead in Calcutta, they were buried in four lines under Mount Perdu.

Therefore I can only advise my countrymen if they are desirous of keeping informed about events in the world in general, and in the Commonwealth in particular, not to come to France in July, unless they are prepared to see the Commonwealth submit to the humiliating laws of 'Queen Bicycle'.[1]

---

of his team according to a very carefully prepared technique, which leaves no chink for indiscreet eyes. With the French, on the contrary, this technique of surrounding is far more lax and, according to the Major, constitutes an invitation to see a bit more.

1. A passionate debate opened at this moment between the Major and his French collaborator, when the latter recalled that one day when he was passing through London, feeling very worried about the international situation, he had been alarmed by a newspaper heading which summed it up in these terms:

ENGLAND'S DESPERATE POSITION

which to a Frenchman meant '*L'Angleterre dans une situation désespérée*'. An illuminating sub-title: '*In spite of 6–3 be proud of old England*' shed a strange light on the question. The Major's collaborator thought that a grave decision had been taken, when his eye was caught by the little square space reserved for stop press news where he read:

TEST SCORES

ENGLAND: FIRST INNINGS 435. HUTTON 169, COMPTON 64.
RAMADIN 6–113, ATKINSON 3–78.
FALL OF WICKETS: 1–1, 2–12, 3–16, ETC.

which explained everything.

A few days later when I spoke of the Tour de France
to my friend Colonel Turlot, confessing that I couldn't
understand anything about it, he retaliated by revealing that after having made three attempts to understand something about a cricket match he had had to
undergo a lengthy treatment with a psychiatrist. He
added:

'Do you know, my dear Thompson, that millions
of *sportifs* daily follow the tour with enthusiasm?'

'Do you mean, my dear Turlot, that they follow the
competitors on their bicycles?'

M. Turlot looked at me as if he thought I was
joking. No. Certainly the *sportifs* he spoke of fought
every day, but that was merely to buy the Late Extra
Special, or to have the best place to see the finish.

I discovered there a fresh and fundamental difference
between our two countries. The English call themselves sportsmen when they practise some sport: the
French call themselves sportsmen when they look on.
So that, painful as the truth may seem to my countrymen, *there are more sportsmen in France than in England*.
Moreover, it couldn't be said that the French don't go
in for sport because they are only onlookers. At the
cinema, for example, especially at the time of the Tour
de France, M. Charnelet comes in really to relax. And
then after the news, there he is, obliged to climb on
his bicycle and to cover 700 kilometres of the route

On making inquiries he learned that the desperate situation was
England's in football, when for the first time in ninety years she had
been beaten by Hungary (6–3). And the stop press was about cricket.

'How can you,' said the Major, 'compare an historic match which
was a national humiliation with your damned bicycle race?'

The Major's face having become purple in a symptomatic fashion,
as also the blue line of his temples which made up the British flag in
the great days, it seemed better to avoid an explosion and close the
discussion.

'Manoeuvres or No Ma

'*…uvres, You Stay Put*'

(for though the competitors cover only one stage at a time, the spectator has to absorb five or six, and, whether he wants to or not, has to climb Mt Galibier or go down the Col d'Albos). M. Charnelet, whose wishes have not been consulted, is obliged to keep on, over the frightful cobblestones of Normandy, he has a puncture in the neighbourhood of Longwy, skids, sets off again, though he has dropped behind, kisses an Alsatian girl on the way, in spite of his boils climbs up the treacherous hairpin bends of Mt Ventoux, and, as a final penalty, crosses the desolate waste land of the Crau.

There is nothing so exhausting as to be forced to cross the Crau in a cinema in the Champs-Élysées at about 22.30 hours. The group straggles, the group dawdles, the group re-forms, the group gets mixed up. It is estimated that there are a million Frenchmen who mentally incorporate themselves in this company, and feel for a moment that they have the legs – what did I say? – I mean the golden flexed muscles of Garraldi or the Demon of the Hills, or the relentless calves of Biquet, that plucky little Frenchman whose luck so often deserts him but who can do wonders at the critical moment.

In the stadiums, at the ringside, or around tennis courts, the French have a way of gesticulating, struggling and generally taking exercise, which contrasts pretty strongly with the attitude of a normal Englishman. Take a boxing match in France and England. It looks like the same sport. In reality it is two very different things. England was the cradle of boxing and other sports. Boxing, tennis, football, golf, are all English children. With the passage of time they have

become emancipated, they have travelled, they have
been made to marry beneath them. The purity of their
essence has been polluted. Between those elderly spinsters who, in order to see the Wimbledon finals, spend
the night on camp stools discussing Drobny's drop
shot or Rosewall's back hand as they would a stitch
in knitting, and the young fans round the Roland-
Garros courts, who call faults *carottes* and lobs
chandelles (especially if it is a foreigner who does
them), there is an almost interstellar difference. No
matter! Whatever Colonel Turlot may say, the sport's
ancestors are English.[1] The noble art of delivering
blows and avoiding them was already honoured under
William the Conqueror while the French were still
fighting with their feet round the gates of Paris. Today
what happens? What we go to see takes place in the
ring. In Paris they fight in the *salle*. With us you could
hear a pin drop. In France you wouldn't hear a
machine-gun. In England gentlemen in dinner jackets
gravely discuss the great value of evasive action, and
the referee is respected like a god. In France the only
thing which is respected is attack, and the referee is

1. Colonel Turlot, who was present, now violently attacked the
Major. Armed with a *Larousse* he dealt him many a formidable diction-
ary blow. 'Cricket,' he read feverishly, 'favourite exercise with the
English, is in reality only a modification of the ancient French game
of *la crosse*. Is sometimes written in the French fashion, *criquet. . . .*'
   'Ridiculous!' cried the Major.
   'Golf,' continued the Colonel, with the utmost calm, 'very possibly
owes its origin to the old French game *le mail*.'
   'Preposterous! Absurd!' sneered the Major.
   'Tennis,' continued the Colonel, with imperturbability, 'developed
out of the old French game *la longue paume*.'
   'Everyone knows that lawn tennis was invented by my ancestor
Major Wingfield in 1874,' exploded the Major, getting very red, and
to avoid worse happenings he went off to get some tea.
   'Tea,' he emphasized, slamming the door.

argued with, insulted, abused: he is an enemy. Finally, while the French hurl sarcastic taunts at the weaker combatant, the English encourage him.

This respect for the weaker competitor, and the almost instinctive desire to give him a chance, are the unwritten laws of the Realm, and are obeyed in the same way by fishermen and huntsmen. To discredit someone for ever, an Englishman will say of him: 'He's shooting a sitting bird.' I am alarmed by the knowledge that in France this rule that a bird when on the ground must not be shot is – I am told – not always respected, though, of course, I don't believe it.[1]

An Englishman's fishing is directed by this same difficult cult. On parts of the Test, one of the noblest waters in Hampshire, it is considered a crime to fish the 'evening rise'; at the very moment when the light fades and the trout become 'easier', the gentleman who has spent the day in torrid heat lying in wait for a fish packs up and goes back to London. Need I add that to use a worm for bait is a dreadful crime, and that the pseudo-sportsmen who use a wet fly are looked at askance?

I do not doubt that French sportsmen are moved by an equal desire for fairness. Yet they are so different. When an Englishman lands the salmon of his life, he has it stuffed. The Frenchman eats it, after being photographed with his catch. If an Englishman catches an undersized trout, he throws it back. A Frenchman would rather eat it. The Frenchman always eats, not because he is hungry, but – apart from that fear of being ridiculous, which haunts us so little and affects

1. Rather a hypocritical remark, since the Major is entirely convinced of the contrary.

Jules Introduces the English Style of Fishing

him so much, if he comes home empty-handed – because any amusement seems silly to him if it does not serve some purpose.

Such utilitarian preoccupations do not affect us. But it is repugnant to the French to do things which aren't useful. (I have been told that they have three children rather than two, not through carelessness but because of the family allowance.) A father makes his son learn English, not for the beauty of the language (always a relative affair in the eyes of a Frenchman), but because *cela peut lui servir plus tard*[1] – it may be useful later on. In the Turlot family there is always a son who learns German so that he can be an interpreter in time of war.

Unlike the French, the English adore doing things which, strictly speaking, serve no purpose. It is only in affairs of the heart that they hate doing anything superfluous, like paying court, or even making love. But as soon as it's a question of serious enterprises like fishing and shooting, even the most modest of them will ruin himself by expending vast reserves of uselessness for the love[2] of sport.

Much more could be said about the way sport is treated by the English and ill-treated by the French. I now perceive that after having written a great deal, I have not yet said anything about the sport which the greatest number of Frenchmen enjoy (two million as against two hundred thousand who play bowls). I mean motoring. That in itself calls for special con-

1. Quoted in French. The Major was annoyed by the doubt expressed in this opinion and refused to translate it.

2. The French may be indifferent fishermen, yet they are masters in the art of playing their catch when they are courting a woman, and they are unequalled in getting what they want with women by discusing Proust or the cinema. (*Major's note.*)

sideration and deserves to be studied in some quiet corner where one can meditate on the subject without any risk of being run over. Perhaps you will have this good fortune or perhaps you can read between the (traffic) lines. . . .

xiii

France at the Steering Wheel

BEWARE of the French in general but particularly on the French roads.

It is essential for an Englishman arriving in France to realize at once that there are two kinds of French-men: those who go on foot, and those who go in cars. The on-foot loathe the in-cars, and the in-cars terror ize the on-foot, though the first pass instantaneously into the camp of the second the moment their hands are on a steering wheel. (It is the same at the theatre with late-comers: after disturbing a dozen people in order to get to their seats, they are the first to protest about those who have the cheek to arrive later.)

The English on the whole drive badly but prudently. The French on the whole drive well but wildly. The proportion of accidents in the two countries is about the same. But I feel more comfortable with people who do good things badly than with those who do bad things well.

The English (and Americans) have long been con-vinced that a car travels less quickly than an aeroplane.

The French (and most of the Latins) still seem determined to prove the contrary.

In the heart of many a Frenchman there slumbers a Nuvolari ready to be awakened by the mere contact of his foot with the accelerator. The peaceful citizen who kindly invited you into his car can be metamorphosed under your very eyes into a demoniacal driver. Jerome Charnelet, that kind of family man who wouldn't squash a fly on a window pane, is quite ready to flatten out one pedestrian per mile provided he feels within his rights. At the green light he sees red. Then nothing will stop him, not even the amber one. On the road this man you thought so steady-going steadily refuses to make way for anyone. It is only when he is absolutely obliged to, and after a brisk fire of hooting, that with very ill grace he will consent to leave the middle of the road. (The English keep to the left. Most people keep to the right. The French opt for the middle, which this time is not the *juste milieu,* happy mean.)

The mere fact of being overtaken puts M. Charnelet in a vile temper. He recaptures his serenity only when he overtakes some new rival. Meanwhile, all his family has to do is to behave well. Woe betide Mme Charnelet if, when asked for it, she can't discover in the car the 'Southern Half of France' which he left behind with the map carrier on the drawing-room chimney-piece. Woe betide her if she doesn't instantly answer the question 'Avallon-Châlons, how far?' Even if she does answer, M. Charnelet, five foot eight of sadism once his foot is on the accelerator, is already enjoying the pleasure he will get out of proving that her calculations are wrong. The children, too, are well trained, 'When your father's thirsty you shall have a drink.' Above all, no untimely stops, 'You should have done it before,' says M. Charnelet. They suffer in silence in honour of that all-powerful goddess of the average Frenchman: Average Speed.

When an English motorist prepares to do 300 miles in England, he thinks about doing 300 miles.

When a Frenchman gets into his car to do 600

kilometres, two-thirds of his mind is taken up with his average speed, the other third is filled with asterisks and forks. I mean those famous symbols in his beloved Michelin. His dream, after having kept up an average of 90 for three hours, is to find a restaurant ✗✗✗ ✿ ✿ if possible in a site *** near a 🛏 (trustworthy) to check the sparking plugs and the oil.

The Englishman will just allow himself to think about a 🛏 after drinking some good *t*. That is if he stays in England. If he goes to France he must first of all force himself to drive on the right side of the road, which in his eyes is the wrong side. That is the most delicate problem. The French have a way of keeping to the right, while continually sliding to the left, which strongly recalls their leanings in politics: the staunchest conservatives refuse to be called 'right' at any price. That's why when an English motorist gets to France, he has some difficulty in knowing where to drive. In reality he would have to push on to Kenya before meeting again with normal people who drive on the left, calculate in miles, use avoirdupois weights and measures, and whose normal temperature is 98·4.[1] Meanwhile, he must accustom himself to that monotonous metric-system zone, which leaves no room for the glorious uncertainty of our old measures: ounce, bushel or peck. A kilometre is always stupidly a thousand metres, whereas with us the mile is marvellously eight furlongs, a furlong two hundred and twenty yards, a yard three feet, a foot twelve inches ... It is true that the *Perfect Travellers' Pocket-Book* puts things right by reminding him that to transfer centigrade into fahrenheit 'you merely multiply by 9 divide by 5 and add 32 degrees'. As for

1. Fahrenheit, of course. (*Major's note.*)

French Motorists – All Certifiable?

converting kilometres into miles it's even easier:
'Multiply by 5 and divide by 8.'[1]

During one of my first tours in France, when I was
suffering from the combined effects of a bad chill and
an even worse crossing, I thought I would stop at a
hotel in Calais and take my temperature. As the
thermometer registered only 40·3 I set out again in
all confidence, raising the hood of my car, and was
rolling pleasantly along with the windscreen open
when I remembered I was among those damned Con-
tinentals who can never do anything like anybody else.
I immediately applied myself to converting my continental temperature into fahrenheit and kilometres
into miles.

I was about to multiply 274 by 5, to divide by 9
and add 32 degrees to the distance between Calais and
Paris, when the sight of another car coming in the
opposite direction on the same side of the road as myself made me suddenly realize that, lost as I was in
my calculations, I had forgotten to drive on the right.
I changed over to the right side and braked in time,
while my *vis-à-vis* pulling up just short of me assailed
me point blank: 'Completely cracked, you old idiot?
Think you're still among the *rosbifs*?'

Then, taking my silence for incomprehension, he
let in the clutch and looked at me, tapping his forehead
with his forefinger.

I was soon to learn that this gesture is a veritable
rite.

Many a time since then I have been on the road with

1. Once again, the Major is not inventing. These practical hints are
given in the *Travellers' Foreign Phrase Book* by J. O. Ketteridge,
F.S.A.A., for the use of the English, already mentioned, p. 125.

M. Taupin or M. Charnelet and have seen them, for reasons which were often obscure, glare at a motorist they were passing, tapping their foreheads the while. Very often the one who is overtaken catches up with M. Taupin and for a no less mysterious motive speaks to him in the same dumb language, though this time he uses his first finger like a kind of screwdriver on his temple. I have deduced from this that the French spend their time on the roads asking one another if they aren't mad, and nearly always find someone at once to confirm that they are.

It is curious to note that a large number of people who, armed with the approved dictionary, are ready to do battle for their idea of 'correct' language are apt to lose all verbal restraint and all sense of propriety as soon as they are in a car. The French, who are born grammarians as others are born navigators or musicians, abandon syntax immediately they are at the wheel.[1] M. Taupin, who devours the column in his newspaper devoted to the defence of the French language, and would not hesitate to reprimand a journalist who wrote *partir à,* instead of *partir pour,* then gets through an impressive consumption of *tête de lard* or *peau de fesse.* In the land of moderation it is always surprising to see people losing their self-control. But the fact of losing it with their hands on the wheel may be pregnant with grave consequences. At least one must do them this justice; you hear them

1. It is easy to see, then, why the French were so surprised by the public apology which appeared lately in the agony column of *The Times,* from a repentant motorist to one of his countrymen on whom he launched a rather violent epithet. A Frenchman would rather have sought to catch up with his adversary and say a bit more, or by means of some skilfully executed wobbling make him collide with a plane tree. (*Major's note.*)

coming a long way off. The golden rule for English motorists is to pass unnoticed. The Frenchman's aim is rather to alarm everyone on the road until there is nobody to be seen. To achieve this he makes as much noise as possible. Most of the world's motor-cars run on petrol. French cars drive on their horns. Especially when they are stopped.[1]

One might think that the Frenchman's speed appetite was determined by the horse-power of his car. That is an error. The smaller his car the faster he wants to go. In this realm of paradox the least dangerous cars are the most powerful ones: their drivers, having become blasé, are the only ones who enjoy the luxury of driving well within the maximum, and of accelerating without effort.

As for Frenchwomen, one must do them this justice: they do drive more slowly than the men. An Englishman might therefore logically believe he would be safer with them. That's another error. In a country where everyone goes so fast this very slowness constitutes a most terrible danger. Add to that a certain variability in pace, and that charming spirit of indecision from which one may deduce from the left trafficator

1. This is an undisguised allusion to Paris blocks [pre-1954]. With the English, hooting means making an improper noise. The horn, whose use in France is a duty or a pastime, can be used in England only in emergency. I was in the Major's *Austin of England* in London one day when I felt I should like to smoke. By accident, instead of pressing the cigarette lighter, I leant on the horn. I was at once overwhelmed with withering glances from ten pairs of eyes (not counting the Major's). I wished I could have hidden under the bonnet.

On the road, the English driver, sacrificing safety to courtesy, never takes his eyes off the rear-mirror. If he sees another car preparing to pass him he waves him on as soon as the road is clear. No need for a horn. Of course there are the cars coming in the opposite direction at a turn of the road. But the drivers would die ràther than hoot. Very often they die in this way.

that the driver-ess is going to turn right (though it isn't quite certain), and you will realize that there is nothing so hazardous as being driven by a woman. . . .

There exists, however, a super-danger in this country where, as in many others, women don't know how to smoke or drive: that is, women who smoke while they are driving.

The safest thing to do, if unfortunately, you are threatened with this smiling menace, is to stop at the nearest town and take the train.

xiv

Fine Sundays

Iᴛ is not improper to suppose that if England hasn't been invaded since 1066 it is because foreigners are afraid of having to spend Sunday there.

It is permissible – on comparing the English Sunday which constrains you to boredom with the French Sunday which drives you to enjoyment – to wonder which of the two is the harder to endure.

Many Frenchmen pass the week asking themselves what they will do on Sunday. Sunday usually arrives before they have answered the question. At least that is what happens with the Taupins and the Robillards, who many a time have confessed to me: '*Que voulez-vous?* On Sunday one doesn't know what on earth to do.'

You never suffer from that kind of hesitation in England, where there is hardly anything to do on Sunday except think about what you will do in the week.

To tell the truth I know no more depressed or depressing sight than M. Robillard's Sunday expression as he pushes his latest-born in his pram along the Champs-Élysées, giving his eldest a smack because he crossed the road alone, catching hold of the little girl because she doesn't want to cross at all, calling out to Madame who is attracted by the shop windows: 'Are you coming on or not?' reaching the Bois at last in the midst of a stream of walkers whose expression is curiously – I nearly wrote furiously – like his own. All these people who walk, walk on and on, until they reach a certain point where they stop, sit down and begin looking at the people walking towards other points, while those who move on look at the seated ones looking at them passing by.

On Sunday half France looks at the other half.

Parisians in country clothes visit their country cousins disguised for the occasion in their town clothes. The former are astonished at the sight of so much black cloth and so many white collars among the cows and clover; the latter observe with some mistrust these pseudo-English in tweeds.

At the end of fine days, the car-travellers back from the country look with some contempt at the on-foot who have had to be content with the air of the Bois, and who grin jeeringly at this procession of agglutinated cars, asking themselves if you don't have to be a bit dotty to go and join a queue on the by-pass. Meanwhile, the mass of *sportifs* – those who go to the races and can't understand how anyone can spend a Sunday watching people kick a ball about, and those in the stadiums who wonder what pleasure there can be in entrusting one's money to horses – become momentary allies in a general contempt for their fellow citizens who waste their time on the roads or in the avenues.

In summer, seated on cane-bottomed chairs extracted from their lairs, the concierges lie in wait for, comment upon, and check those returning home.

A few individualists, moved by the spirit of contradiction rather than by any deep-rooted taste, decide to stay at home and knock in a few nails, tidy up the things they've disarranged, or devote themselves to the national sport of 'pottering about' which consists essentially in making out of old junk and with an expenditure of immense toil articles which can be bought brand new and cheaply over the counter. 'Pottering about' constitutes an activity in France which is so important it deserves special consideration (I shall come back to it). These partisans of Sunday at home correspond in a certain sense to the mass of British citizens who busy themselves with their gardens or with devouring the divorce reports in the many-paged Sunday newspapers, and to lunching as badly as on any other day, only eating rather more.

In his inscrutable caprice the Creator has made us the opposite of our neighbours right up to the last second of the seventh day.

France and England both have two faces, a week-day one and a Sunday one; but the former shows hers while the second hides it.

On Sundays the Frenchman is careful about his dress. The Englishman neglects his. While his French neighbour dresses up, his tendency is rather to undress.[1] On Sundays the Frenchman shaves more carefully. The Englishman – no, there are no two ways of shaving for an Englishman.

While my compatriots get through this day of immobility at home, wearing their shabbiest clothes, leaving it to a few uneducated *nouveaux riches* to dress correctly, the French, all spruced up, come out of their homes, and display themselves in their finest attire: *le*

---

1. Except to go to Church, if he does go. Generally, in small towns particularly, the English go to Church not so much for the sake of going but to see who didn't go. (*Major's note.*)

costume de dimanche. There is no question of Sunday clothes for an Englishman, unless he is entirely without friends or modesty . . . that is to say, a rarity.

The height of *chic* for a Frenchman is to be *tiré à quatre épingles*,[1] an expression which like *s'endimancher* has no real equivalent in the language of Shakespeare. Compared with the Englishman who still maintains a sporting air in a *smoking* (dinner jacket)[2] the Frenchman maintains a certain formality in sporting clothes and often in plus fours; he doesn't look quite real – like a new recruit distinguishable at a glance from an old soldier because he has not yet settled into his uniform. Perhaps it's because he is insufficiently trousered.

After all, we must know what we are before knowing what we want to be. We had been playing golf for five hundred years when the French Academy was founded in 1635. Isn't it all to the honour and advantage of the French that they look more natural dressed up as Academicians than as golfers?

Differing from his planetary neighbour who likes to shine like a new penny, the Englishman has a horror of anything new and considers it counterfeit. For him true *chic* is inseparable from a certain shabbiness. Formerly, in the days when Frenchmen gave their old clothes to their servants to finish them off, the English dandies used to make their butlers wear their new suits to break them in. Today the *boys of Belgravia*[3] wear their

---

1. The expressions 'dressed up to the nines' or 'just stepped out of a band box', so difficult to translate, have a slightly derogatory meaning. (*Major's note.*)

2. 'Smoking' in French. I mean, of course, a dinner jacket, but in France you must write English as the French do. (*Major's note.*)

3. Expression coined by the Major to indicate the district round Belgrave Square, one of the smartest quarters of London.

new suits secretly until they are fit to be seen. The Frenchman will wear his old things until they are absolutely threadbare and keep his new suit for Sunday.

The English way of living six days a week and dying on Sundays may surprise a foreigner, but that of many Frenchmen who merely exist during the week and come to life on Sundays is no less astonishing.

This anxiety to preserve new things and use them – less for himself than for others – only in the last extremity (which means the week-end) is doubtless one of the characteristics of the Frenchman, who would perhaps be getting rusty unless he polished himself up once a week.

My visit to the Turlots was to reveal other aspects of the foreseeing and careful Frenchman.

XV

Diabolical Inventions of the French

THE first time I arrived at Saumur at my friends the
Turlots', one summer's day, their house in the Rue
Dacier seemed quite dead behind its closed shutters.
The servant who opened the door first made me put on
some queer felt slippers, perhaps to protect the parquet
floor but more likely to make me lose my balance. Then
she ushered me in to a fairly large *salon* impregnated
with the smell of mustiness and cretonne. Although
the sun filtered through the slats in the shutters, I had
to accustom my eyes to the semi-darkness before I
could penetrate the surrounding mystery. On all sides
were white shapes. I guessed at rather than saw several
arm-chairs, a sofa, a grand piano, a chest, something
that looked like a harp, all these objects being swathed
in dust-sheets. A number of pictures hung on the walls,
but it was difficult to know what they represented. Not
that they belonged to a peculiarly surrealist school:
they were covered with newspaper. The only thing
that seemed animated by any movement was the clock.
And even its tick-tock came from under a white shroud
pierced by the arrow of a bronze Cupid. In a corner
over a little table hung two crossed cavalry sabres,
both protected by sheaths of yellow linen. I had evidently come at a bad moment: the Turlots were mov-
ing. Or they had fallen on evil days and were selling
up; the furniture was about to be carted away. My

pessimistic suppositions were ended by the appearance of a grey dust-sheet from which emerged the head of the Colonel: 'Forgive me, my dear Major, I was pottering about.'

I have often wondered what the colonel's 'pottering' really amounted to. Often afterwards I was to find my way into what he called his 'lab' and see him busy with an oscillator and a kind of condenser without, however, guessing what kind of experiments he was conducting. Now I think I can declare that the masterpiece at which he has been working for the last seven years is a wireless set, every bit of which he has assembled with his own hands. It has cost him more than 40,000 francs. On fine days he can hear the programme from the Massif Central. He could get the whole world on a set costing 22,700 francs in any wireless shop. Only a stupid Englishman could fail to notice the difference.

Colonel Turlot's pottering is of the usual handy-man type, but there also exists a *de luxe* pottering, the kind practised by M. Charnelet with his car. As soon as he has brought a car M. Charnelet has one aim: to make it look less like a standard model. With the help of innumerable dealers who each sell him some little thing – a trafficator, reflector mirror, or another badge – saying 'With that it's not just *anybody's* car',[1] M. Charnelot

1. Excellent publicity aid and knock-you-down argument of salesmen in this country where they are always telling you to 'do as everyone else does' but end by persuading you to do as nobody else does. In France they have a horror of being noticed through a panic fear of being ridiculous, but do everything they can to avoid passing unnoticed. The fear of seeming ridiculous (which could not affect an Englishman since, being English, he could not be ridiculous) curbs them, but the desire for manifesting their individuality spurs them on. (*Major's note*).

Technical Hitch

adorns it with all sorts of accessories until when it's re-sprayed it is unrecognizable. Early on Sunday mornings – sometimes on week-days between office hours – he secludes himself and his car in the Bois de Boulogne, brings out his duster, rubs up the chromium, polishes the paintwork, and is annoyed but delighted when an idler prowls round it and finally asks what make it is.

Besides this pottering *de luxe* there is the ordinary, even daily, pottering which is even more fascinating to study: it forms an integral part of the life of every individual. Among its typical manifestations figures the filter, or more precisely the coffee filter. I have often wondered why the Frenchman who could have set before him, ready and hot, the best coffee in the world, prefers to see it drip drop by drop through a mysterious alembic and finally drinks it cold, after burning his fingers in an unsuccessful attempt to regulate the filtering: I can only think he likes to 'potter' with his coffee.[1] The filter is one of those discoveries, one of those diabolical inventions of the French which include the 'Minuterie' (pneumatic stair lighting), automatically closing Métro doors, unperforated money orders, scissors for snipping postal orders, and postal orders waiting to be snipped, restrictive electric light switches (either a ceiling light without the bedside light or the bedside light without the ceiling light), and all those creaking cages or cabins which it is very rash to board

1. The same sort of thing happens with books. Any English or American publisher who thought of forcing buyers to cut each section twice along the top and once down the side would soon be bankrupt. In France, on the contrary, certain publishers who wished to make an innovation and present books already cut to the public, had to revert quickly to the old formula which alone could satisfy *real readers*. In the same way, but to a lesser degree, certain real (French) smokers claim that the only real cigarettes are those you make yourself. (*Major's note.*)

without reading the OPERATING INSTRUCTIONS, and which, under the name of lifts, achieve the noble distinction of remaining the one means of locomotion which is slower than one's own feet.

Of all the diabolical inventions of the French, one deserves the palm: I refer to those places which the French who love a paradox call 'conveniences' and which they have ingeniously rendered the most inconvenient in the world.[1] First, those in Paris – so intimately connected with the telephone in cafés that sometimes one isn't quite sure what kind of communication one is meant to establish. (The sight of a pale saucer in the middle of which a twenty-franc piece appeals desperately for a sister coin reminds you that you are in the Realm of the Tip.) The country ones – tiny cells which you only reach after fighting your way through a no-man's-land of hens and old iron – are obscure abysses where you keep your balance only by an acrobatic miracle and where you need all the cunning of a Red Indian to escape the blind vindictiveness of a maelstrom which, in the guise of a flush, makes you bolt for a door so constructed that, instead of opening on to the dry light, it pushes you back into the damp darkness.

Excuse this digression which took me away for a moment. It was necessary. I now come back to Saumur and Colonel Turlot and his dust-sheets and his jobs. Having covered up one of the strange machines in his 'lab' with a camouflage-sheet, probably scrounged from some Allies Surplus Depot, the Colonel took off

1. Obviously I wouldn't broach such a subject in England, but since I am in the country of Rabelais I think I can take a chance. (*Major's note.*)

his overall and hung it on a nail, then extracting his
hunter from a washleather case exclaimed: 'Good
Lord! twelve o'clock already. Have you seen the
Missis?'

We went to look for her. I thought the Colonel was
about to produce his wife from a dust-sheet when half
of Mme Turlot emerged from a cupboard. Clad in a
blue overall, with her head tied up in a scarf, she was
putting away a tailor-made with an astrakhan collar in
a moth-proof bag.

'Madame's latest extravagance,' said the Colonel.
'Of course she doesn't wear it here except on special
occasions . . . It's really for going to Paris.'

Mme Turlot begged me to excuse her. She really
wasn't presentable. She was going to put on a dress
and get ready for lunch. I was sorry my arrival had
obviously thrown the household into a state of some
perturbation. The Turlots, who have a large house,
were preparing to lunch in the kitchen, but in my
honour undertook to deshroud the dining-room and
the famous haunted *salon* with its spectral furniture
into which they never ventured when they were alone.

'We'll open a nice bottle for you, my dear Major,'
said the Colonel, who owns a very good cellar but
drinks every day a red *vin ordinaire*.

It may seem dangerous to judge a country by
appearances, especially when that is hidden under a
dust-sheet, and I have no doubt that the French in
general make a less systematic use of the dust-sheet
than the Turlots do. But leaving aside the Colonel, I
cannot help remembering that M. Taupin, like M.
Charnelet, has only one thought when he buys a car:
to put loose covers over the seats. They remove these

the day they sell the car (*perf. cond.*) and if possible use them again in their new one.

I am inclined to believe that the dust-cover is the symbol of the saving – even self-depriving – spirit of the French. These people, who are so greedy of possessions that they will say 'I have my poor'[1] and are more spoiled by life than any others on earth make a veritable cult of hardship, covering up the seats of their cars being one of its most widespread manifestations. I know of a millionaire who made a reputation by taking his meals on a deal table, sending his children to the village school, travelling third class, never cutting a piece of string, and saying to any of his employees who asked for a rise: 'I can't think how you manage to spend so much!'

In the land of plenty the real, most solid wealth attires itself in humility: only poor people spend recklessly.[2]

1. Compare this expression with the 'I always give to the Salvation Army', loudly proclaimed by M. Charnelet when a salvationist in a blue bonnet comes into the restaurant. Obviously M. Charnelet wants to emphasize his discernment in giving. Direct contact with a down-and-out, especially in a restaurant, makes him uneasy, but the uniform of the Salvation Army is reassuring: he knows where his money goes. (*Major's note.*)

2. To these must be added a few super-rich foreigners whose extravagance, while considered reasonable if it is a question of restoring Versailles, are far more criticized if it's a question of a private fête by night. Yet the strange thing is, in this realm of mistrust and the old stocking, where it is the custom to put something by for bad times, and when the bad times come to continue putting something by for worse ones, there is nothing like a foreigner for getting money out of its hiding places. The people mistrust investments, but at regular intervals we learn that a man whose name ends in *ski* or *vici*, more powerful than any Dupont, has got millions out of them and ruined three centuries of saving. '*It was a long way off . . . no one would ever know*', say the dupes who (always this fear of appearing ridiculous) are careful not to make themselves known when the question of indemnity arises, but settle down this time to depriving themselves in good earnest. (*Major's note.*)

XVI

The Land of Miracles

THE Miracle, together with the vine, is one of the principal products of France.

All Frenchmen – positivists, rationalists, or Voltairians – firmly believe in miracles. When the enemy is at the gates of Paris, or when there is only a minute left to play against England at Colombes, then they rely on Providence, who, it must be admitted, has often spoiled them.

Having, like her Latin sisters, subscribed to miracles from her earliest childhood, France attracts miracles as other countries attract humidity. More than that. She adapts them to the needs of the moment: the miracle which went on foot with Sainte Geneviève, on horseback with Joan of Arc, became motorized with the taxis of the Marne. Tomorrow it may be atomic.

In other countries, when a statesman cries 'Only a miracle can save us,' that's the end of everything. In France it can be the beginning of a great many things. The Frenchman brightens up in darkness, becomes organized in chaos. Possible things do not interest him very much: impossible things impassion him. In the land of facility difficulty is inspiring. The national flower, astuteness, thrives on it.

The miracle follows a Frenchman through life just as it accompanies France throughout her history. The first thing the French (who are cultivated even before

'Look, Elmer, a Statue of Ingrid Bergman!'

they are born) teach their children is that they were discovered in a cabbage. Parents do everything in their power to make their children become miracle-children. Brought up as they are in contact with learned provincial spinsters, indulgent uncles, and philosophic old men, the children of France, very forward for their age, deliver themselves of octogenarian opinions which would drive English parents crazy, but delight the authors of their days who enjoy airing them in public, like an anthology of witty sayings.

The child, on his side, openly or in secret, keeps up this miracle cult. He learns not only of Joan of Arc, and the natural frontiers the Creator marked out for the French, while He left so many others to discover them for themselves;[1] he associates with those heroes of radio, film and comic strip, who find their way through virgin forests, rescue a few (English) explorers from certain death, and come back to France with the secret of the curare bomb, and congratulations from Scotland Yard.

The astuteness of the schoolboy continues to increase until it allows him to perform the miracle known to all Frenchmen – the famous Miracle of the little Broom. In the barracks courtyard, under the vigilant eye of the resolutely unhelpful sergeant, he produces from nowhere a little broom to sweep away the wind. These are the miniature peace-time Battles of the Marne. The Frenchman retains the imprint of this scholasticism till

1. From this point of view, as from so many others, England is of course a land apart. Still I could find no answer to M. Taupin's very strange remark calling my attention to the fact that the first two letters of the word France were those of the English word for liberty: in English (*freedom*), in German (*freiheit*), in Swedish (*frihet*), in Icelandic (*frelsi*), not to mention other languages, and that all this was a sign of some miraculous order of things. (*Major's note.*)

the day of his death, and transmits it to his son, saying, 'You'll see when you do your military service.'

Side by side with the *lycée* and the barracks, the technical schools take charge of the sharpening and embellishing of the Frenchman's astuteness, and he emerges from them as from a conjuror's box of tricks; he grasps at once what so many others understand too late. Sometimes he leaves the country. Then he installs the Métro at Caracas, or introduces frogs to the cuisines of Adelaide. He brings Gascony to Cincinnati, the Polytechnic to Kabul. But he will retire as early as possible to Barcelonette or Brie, because, though there may be many countries for earning one's living, France is, after all, the one where life is best spent.

Land of Miracles, miracle-men, miracle-dresses, Realm of Fine Shades and Imponderables, I am about to leave you. . . .

Soon now I shall fly off to Bengal at the cordial invitation of my old friend Colonel Basil Cranworth who, before taking up his new post at Singapore, has asked me to his last tiger shoot. But I shall not set off as I used to do. A hundred faces, invisible yet present, escort me. Colonel Cranworth and our host the Maharajah of Bhagalpur will not be aware of them, but, while they are talking about man-eaters, Martine's face will hover over the table, I shall think of Martine, I shall think of Paris. And my longing will not only be sentimental. In India, some months ago now, one night I felt the gastric nostalgia of France creeping over me. As I slept in my tent in the torrid monsoon-swept jungle of Assam, old mother Grenouillet appeared to me in a dream: 'What are you up to there, Major?' Standing beside the peaceful waters which know neither monsoon nor typhoon, with her hands on her hips, she asked: 'What would you say, Major, to some of my trout *à la crème?*'

That night I knew I was a changed man.

Yes, it's done now! Whether I'm with the Sikhs or the Zulus, at Rangoon or in Zanzibar, I think of the Place Vendôme and Azay-le-Rideau. And when I come back from India or Kalahari, and the aeroplane, after flying over so many stretches of sand and rock where earth and sky seem to have declared war on one another, brings me nearer the winding Seine, over that little hexagon blessed by the Gods, where everything is done for man's pleasure on man's scale, for the greater delight of his retina, his palate, and his heart, I know I have come back to the Land of Miracles.

Country, unlike any other, whose farms, churches, and country houses fit so well into the landscape that they all seem to have been conceived at the same time.

Land of forty-three million thinking planets, each with its own little idea at the back of its mind, whose citizens – all different and all alike in wanting to be different – argue ceaselessly and in the end conclude:

'Fundamentally we are agreed. . . .'

Country where the people's individuality is so marked that they cannot hear a weather report on the wireless without identifying themselves, joyously with 'set fair', dramatically with 'stormy'.

Strange land, where in one and the same minute I can find someone who hates me and someone who loves me, and realize – and that's the miracle – that they are one and the same person.

Charnelets and Taupins, Turlots and Pochets, all animated by the same spirit of criticism and freedom – I have often spoken ill of you.

Now I must earn your forgiveness.

I have said that you were sceptical, mistrustful, parsimonious. The miracle is that you are also equally enthusiastic, trustful, generous. If tomorrow you were to become disciplined, accurate, silent, a great misfortune would have befallen the world. For your faults are but the reverse side of your qualities. Your nation of xenophobes is a refuge for foreigners, you don't resist fraud yet you bring up your children in the cult of the right road, your race of *petits bourgeois* is a race of *grands seigneurs,* you are the most inhospitable people in the whole universe, and your country the most welcoming on the globe. And if it be true that minds are like parachutes (as Lord Dewar said, to function they must be open), then you are the world's finest parachutists.

Forgive me . . . Forgive my audacity. Looking back over these notes of an explorer who set out to discover France and the French, I am terrified by my temerity . . . What right had I – an Englishman – to catalogue your weaknesses? The miserable right of men who think they are qualified to speak about life on earth while they are mere children when they die, without even having lived to be a hundred? Perhaps simply by the right I learnt from Bernard Shaw: the best way to familiarize yourself with a subject is to write a book about it.

It remains for me to obtain the forgiveness of my Queen.

That good English governess Miss ffyfth teaches the children of the Bois de Boulogne that they are very lucky to be French, for they inhabit the one country in the world which is only twenty-one miles away from England.

May my Sovereign pardon me if I now reverse the axiom: one of the Englishman's privileges is that he need only cross the Channel to be in France. May her Gracious Majesty not hold it against me that I have chosen to live in France. Was it not in my humble way the best I could do to celebrate the *Entente Cordiale*?

Alas! There is more to come, your Majesty, and worse. Nowadays I dawdle in the streets of Paris ... When a car runs into another car (and God knows that happens often enough) I stand and stare ... Then again – dare I admit? – such charming silhouettes pass along the Paris streets, especially in spring ... that ... yes, I find myself turning round. For forty years I saw, now I look. That is not all: the other day, forgetting all my reserve, I allowed myself to ask M. Taupin about that spot on his nose. And when I left him I said '*Au revoir, allez!*' Finally, my Queen, there's that terrible longing for snails that may come over me at Gibraltar or in Bombay, or for that Chambolle-Musigny which old Rougetrogne fetches up from his cellar when I go to Avallon, and which brings out the blue line of my temples against the crimson background of my cheeks so marvellously that the *patron* calls to his little boy, 'Sonny, come and see Major Thompson doing the Union Jack.' Good Heavens, how disgraceful, your Majesty! I am indeed damned. God will punish me one day by making me disintegrate on the banks of the Cousin or the Midouze.

Meanwhile I confess: hills of Burgundy, blue distances of the Île de France, quays of Paris, provinces of Saint-Louis en l'Île, I am your docile slave.

O France! where we can put up so comfortably and have such good meals, how often now have I unfolded your map with its names so full of promise: Brocéliande, Vézelay, Brantôme, Loctudy, and all those anonymous but individual La Fertés with the old maids gossiping behind the curtains, and all the pretty girls who seem to have been created just to give the old maids something to gossip about . . . O France! I love your speech, I love your sky, I love your light, I love your stubborn spirit.

I love everything about you and you in everything. *F* for folly, *r* for reason, *a* for amour, *n* for nanny, *c* for chauvin, *e* for Ernest . . . I love France.

*Some other
light-hearted Penguins
are described on the
following pages*

TWO POPULAR HUMORISTS

JEROME K. JEROME
Three Men in a Boat
1213

The author writes of this book: 'The world has been very kind ... It has been translated into, I think, every European language, also into some of those of Asia ... It is as the author of *Three Men in a Boat* (*to say nothing of the Dog*) that the public persists in remembering me.' The reality and humour of the story, together with the many expressions of Jerome's philosophy of life, will convince the reader that the enthusiasm is justified.

W. W. JACOBS
Selected Short Stories
1345

The humour of W. W. Jacobs is in the masculine English tradition which immortalizes the comic characters of Shakespeare, Dickens, and the Grossmiths. Of the stories in this volume, fourteen are concerned with the wharfside life he knew so well in the London of four-wheelers. The night-watchman has a fund of tales about Sam Small, Ginger Dick, and Peter Russet. Another fertile source of stories is the *Cauliflower*, the pub at Claybury patronized by artful Bob Pretty. The selection has a double appeal: as a period piece, and as perennial comedy.

BETTY MACDONALD

The Egg and I

1160

The Egg and I is the famous story of Betty Macdonald's life on a chicken ranch in the North Pacific coast country of California. Much of her time was spent doing menial tasks in primitive conditions, but in spite of irritations and disappointments she has an eye for 'the funny side' of situations and people.

'This book is rattlingly well-written, brims with types, and is very funny. I recommend it to everyone.' – *Observer*.

The Plague and I

1394

Even Betty's sense of humour and proportion fail when she learns that she has T.B. and must go to a sanatorium. But her buoyancy soon re-asserts itself, and she finds material for infectious laughter among staff and patients. Her gay pen converts the daily routine into delicious entertainment.

'A gay best-seller ... the book is, in the highest sense, high-spirited' – *Peter Quennell*

NOT FOR SALE IN THE U.S.A. OR CANADA